JOHN BROOKS HOME - 1755
Chatham County, N. C.

Surgery in the Eighteenth Century

The Reward of Cruelty—Plate IV of THE FOUR STAGES OF CRUELTY by William Hogarth, showing a dissection at Surgeon's Hall.

THE DIARY *of a* SURGEON IN *the* YEAR 1751-1752

By JOHN KNYVETON, *Licentiate of the* SOCIETY *of* APOTHECARIES; *Doctor of Medicine of the* UNIVERSITY *of* ABERDEEN; *Teacher of Midwifery to & Man Mid-Wife in* INFIRMARY HALL; *Surgeon's Mate,* H.M.S. LANCASTER.

Edited & Transcribed by ERNEST GRAY

D. APPLETON-CENTURY COMPANY
INCORPORATED
NEW YORK 1937 LONDON

PRINTED IN THE UNITED STATES OF AMERICA

CONTENTS

ILLUSTRATIONS

EDITOR'S NOTE

JOHN KNYVETON, the author of the ensuing Journal, was born at Bromley on September 16, 1729, the second son and the third child of Mary and Charles Knyveton, apothecary of that village. His brother, the eldest child, was born in October, 1724, and a sister in May, 1726. John's mother died at his birth, whereupon the father moved to Chatham and opened a surgery and dispensary there. But it did not flourish, and he died two years later from a scratch contracted whilst lancing an abscess. The three children were thereupon adopted by their paternal uncle, George Martin Knyveton, a surgeon residing in the village of Hestley, Kent. This George Knyveton was a distant ancestor of a very close friend of the editor, the leather-bound Journal in which the Diary is written appearing whilst helping this friend sort out some old family records, and being presented to him, as one especially interested in the History of Medicine.

The two brothers were both intended for their father's profession, and accordingly, in keeping with the custom of the times, were duly apprenticed on reaching "years of discretion"—seventeen in the case of John, eighteen in that of his brother—to their uncle, with whom they saw practice for some years before coming to London to polish off their knowledge by taking a short hospital course of six months to a year at one of the big London infirmaries.

In those days the foundations of the modern medical training were being laid down. Physicians and surgeons as a whole were growing tired of the dogmatism of the ancient authorities—Aristotle, Hippocrates, and Galen, whose theories had held sway for some five hundred years—and were beginning to think for themselves, aided thereto by the microscope, then just emerging from obscurity. At the close of the seventeenth century an English physician named Sydenham had published a book urging the medical profession to "go back to the bedside"—found their theories upon the symptoms they found in the patient—stressing, in a word, the vital importance of clinical experience. This had not hitherto been the case. Galen died in A.D. 200, but his view that the body was composed of certain "Humours" (originally four in number), disease resulting from absence or overproduction of one especial "Humour," dominated the medical outlook, as we have said, for five hundred years. The mass of physicians, soaked in this dogmatism, did not study their patients' symptoms, but assumed merely that one of his "vital elements" was missing or being overproductive, and treated him accordingly. When at last the patient came to be studied, many strange discrepancies were found. John Knyveton was taught the old humoral theory as the causation of disease, but he was also sent to study the patients in the wards of a big hospital; and he must have noticed many anomalies, the text-books of his day being a jumble of Galen's dogmatism patched with scraps of the new knowledge then available.

But it is difficult enough for us in these days of asepsis and sanitation to realise the then state of affairs in a hospital, without engaging in these academic matters. There was no sanitation system at all; and since fresh air was considered dangerous, the windows were always kept tightly shut. Baths were infrequent, and largely considered harmful; and even the gentry then stank in a manner that would make a modern tramp blush. Lice and dirt were everywhere, and since nothing was known of bacteriology the simplest wound inflicted by a surgeon suppurated and healed slowly by granulation only. For this reason the surgeons when faced with an extensive wound endeavoured to obtain a plane surface that they could purify with the cautery, that is, fire. Thus if you broke your leg, and the bone protruded, off the limb came; and since there were no anæsthetics, you had to bear the pain as best you might, many dying from the agony and the shock. The interior of the body was, of course, a Forbidden Kingdom; those suffering from an appendicitis or a twisted bowel died as speedily as they could to end their sufferings, the surgeon watching sympathetically but helplessly. Dentists heroically attempted to treat the rottenness of a tooth by burning out the blackened portion with a hot wire, subsequently filling the hole—if the patient would let them—with molten lead or gold. True to the Galenic theory, bleeding was a panacea for all ills, for it relieved the body of the particular "Humour" oppressing it, and left the body more free to battle with what was left. Wounds were encouraged to suppurate that the body might the quicker rid itself of its base portions.

Bearing all these things in mind, the hospital of those days can better be imagined than described; and because of them the present editor, whilst letting the main portion of the Diary speak for itself has thought fit to alter the names of many that appear in it, and above all the name and position of the hospital at which John Knyveton attended. The conditions at "Infirmary Hall" were those of every hospital at the time, but there are those who might think the editor had some axe of his own to grind were he to allow the hospital to be named, this being an age of impudent literary allusions.

One other point remains. A prospective surgeon

or physician was, as we have said, apprenticed to a practitioner for a number of years before rounding off his training at a university or hospital. The medical profession of those days had a very low standing, and it was possible for a student after only six months or so at an infirmary to obtain a diploma that was little more than a license to practise. Physic he learned from the man to whom he had been apprenticed; anatomy was the remaining important subject; without its aid surgery could not be learnt; and the student might take it either at the hospital whose wards he walked—as did John Knyveton's brother at St. George's Hospital—or at the private house of some physician or surgeon attached to the hospital, as did John himself. In this latter case a word from that particular physician or surgeon would often gain a student a license; as John found when after spending all his money in six months he was faced with the prospect of finding employment.

John Knyveton after many vicissitudes came back again to London, and settled in Oxendon Street, Haymarket; taking the Doctorate of Medicine of Aberdeen University, and becoming teacher of Midwifery to his old hospital, Infirmary Hall; marrying in 1763 Elizabeth Brodie, daughter of Mr. Brodie, an army linen-draper. He writes of his wife that "her manners are amiable, her Disposition gentle, her Understanding naturally good, improved by reading and the conversation of reasonable people." He died in 1809. The present volume covers only the first year of his life as a surgeon.

ERNEST GRAY

Muswell Hill, London

Part One

LONDON

I

September 17.

My last day of apprenticeship with my uncle. The house in a great bustle, my aunt and the maids ironing my linen and packing my box. My uncle very solemn uttering frequent remarks anent the Dignity of Labour and the Virtue of an Honest Life; the last shown by his charging Saml. Potter 5/— for drawing three teeth, only one of which he extracted himself. the other two being drawn by yr. obdt. servant. Noted that the worthy Saml. kept tight hold of his wife's wrist so that her squeals nigh drowned his as I pulled. After supper my uncle still very solemn hands over to me the money bequeathed me by my father, in all some £75, and then after more talk falls to his knees, my aunt with him, and invokes a Blessing.

To bed with my head in a Whirl, and could hardly sleep for thinking of my new breeches and braided coat.

September 18.

Up betimes to catch the coach, on which my uncle had taken me an outside seat. The last present he gives me were a set of ivory-handled lancets very fine, and then the coach arriving I was bustled on to it, my aunt nigh taking all the starch out of my ruffles with her tears. A fine morning, and the company on the coach very agreeable, passing tales, and one gentleman a flask of Eau-de-Vie, of which the guard partook heartily, so that his tunes on his horn became ever more frequent and lusty. Dined off a leg of mutton at a tolerable Inn whose name I have forgot, though it had a Crown in it. The plump gentleman with the flask very hearty, and playful with the serving wench. To coach once more, and so to London, which we approached in a smother of rain about nine o'clock, the city very fine as it grew before us a great dark mass all twinkling with lights. Was 'mazed to find the streets thronged with folk and all lit up despite the lateness of the hour; they were as bright as noon-day with the horn lanterns in the shops and Inns, and with the flambeaux carried by the chair-men; these worthies swearing and crying out in a manner that would have earned them the stocks at home. My journey not finished even when we arrived at the posting house, but to hackney coach and so to Mr. Hunt's, the barber, of Dean Street, Soho, with whom I am to lodge. Reached there after a vile tedious journey of nigh an hour, Mr. Hunt a very worthy man, his wife pitted with the Small Pox. The room to which they showed me tolerable comfortable, but am doubtful whether I shall sleep much, what with the street noises and the rumble of the coaches over the cobbles, very different to the rustic solitude of my beloved country home. Unpacked, and so to bed, scratching at a flea contracted from that jail of a coach.

September 19.

Woke early this morning by the cries of Milk-O! and the noise of market carts entering the town. Rose hastily in some excitement and to view through my window, being pleased to find thereat a fine prospect of trees and meadows, which Mr. Hunt later informs me are the Tottenham Fields, and beyond them the hills of Highgate and Hampstead; the last of interest to a Physician, as from them bubble certain springs whose waters are very healthful for the stone and surfeit, and the like complaints. They are much sought after, I learn, by the gallants and ladies of the town, who seek in them to renew that Youth they dissipate so elegantly at routes and gaming. Did not gaze long, my attention being catched by a wench lacing herself at the window of a neighbouring house the saucy quean smiling at me. Upon which with remembrance of certain of my uncle's advice, did retire and taking out the second volume of Doctor Sydenham's Treatise did read therein with much comfort and profit until summoned down by my host to break my fast.

Am to pay him 10/6 per week for lodging and board, washing to be extra and I doubt not that he will have a hard bargain of it the Lord having favoured me with a hearty relish for my vittles. Much discourse at meat concerning my brother, now practising in Yorkshire, and who did lodge with Mr. Hunt some three years back when himself studying for the golden mantle of Æsculapius. Mr. Hunt warns me that if I am to be much abroad it will be as well to buy myself a cudgel or better small sword as to the west of us beyond the Marylebone Gardens thieves and gentlemen of the road do swarm in great abundance attracted thereto by the many houses of the rich in that quarter, and they do pass even in day into the streets of the town to the great annoyance of the passers by. He informs me that quite recently some few months back the coach of my Lady Albemarle was robbed in Great Russell Street in broad day by nine men, the King compensating her for her loss the next day by giving her a gold watch and chain, very fine. And so to take my leave and into the street with many directions from my worthy host and his spouse as how to find my way to Infirmary Hall where I am to bring the knowledge imparted by my dear uncle in my four years apprenticeship to its full completion. On my way thither called at the house of Doctor Urquehart the anatomist, with whom I am to take Anatomy and Chirurgery or Surgery as it is more commonly called, to find the doctor already gone ahead to the Hall. Noted that he had a tolerable fine house with a large outbuilding at the back, which I doubt not is his dissecting room and with which I hope to become well acquaint before my time is served. And so on through the Park, where I saw some gentlemen very fine riding.

Infirmary Hall a very large building and with the swarm of beggars and quack salvers about its gates I was hard put to it to find the entrance. This I did at last however by enquiring the way of a short youth with a disgraceful cravat who informed me he had been very drunk the night before. I offered to bleed him but with great flow of language he informed me that he was a doctor himself and quite capable of treating his own complaints, and so I introduced myself to him, his choler abating to find I was pursuing the same quest as he. With him to the lobby of the Infirmary where we found the lecturers for this session exhibiting their cards and questing for members for their lectures. My short friend informs me that Doctor Urquehart is one of the best teachers of Anatomy in London town and I found his knowledge very useful, as it saved me from the importunities of other teachers whose skill and knowledge was as small as their conceit was great. Arranged however with one gentleman in a fine peruke to take a course in Vegetable and Animal Anatomy and Physiology this to help me with my Materia Medica and thereby parted with the sum of five guineas. Doctor Urquehart was then performing an amputation of the thigh upon a porter brought in that morning from Covent Garden with a compounded fracture of the left femur the result of a kick from a horse. My new found friend enquiring whether I had seen much surgery takes me through a long corridor with a heavy mephitic stench to a room at the far end lit by a large sky-light. Here we found my future teacher already begun upon his patient, the latter being tied down upon a large table, not so clean as the one my uncle uses for such purposes, but then in such a place they perform more operations in one week than my uncle performs in a year. The patient being a poor man had few friends able to make him drunk and so he being a well developed specimen many ropes were necessary to control his struggles. Amongst those holding him my friend the drunk gentleman pointed out a once famous pugilist and a very big man suspected of having taken the High Toby but who was employed by Doctor Urquehart and shielded by him from the law because he could lift a coffin from its bed single-handed; a useful accomplishment in these otherwise enlightened days, when the poor surgeon must rely for the advancement of his art upon the fruit of the gallows-tree and what he can snatch from the graveyards.

The incisions of Doctor Urquehart placed high up on the thigh there was considerable trouble from the mass of muscle to find the great arteries, which the Doctor for his own advancement wished to ligature with cords, though I learn that in such Institutions it is quite common to cauterise them only, with a hot iron or with boiling tar. Thus from the plunging of the patient who seemed unable to comprehend that it was done for his own good and the clumsiness of the Infirmary surgeon Mr. Jamie who was more foxed than my friend ten minutes elapsed before the leg lay on the floor, and much blood was shed. I wished to enquire from my short friend what the chances of recovery were, knowing that in such a place they must surely be very small if indeed existent at all, but after one attempt gave it up as the screams of the porter made speech impossible. Later he was removed and sawdust thrown over the floor and on the bigger blood blots on the walls—here again I saw the difference of town and country practice for my uncle could not use much sawdust as the carrier would not consider it the worth of carriage.

Much edified, I turned to find my friend gone, and so to introduce myself to the Doctor then turning down his cuffs and tying a knot in his bob-wig, which had become disarranged, and to give him my letter of introduction from my uncle. He received me kindly for my uncle's sake but could not then spare me much time, as he had much work to perform that morning and was due at a tea-drinking at some fashionable salon the same afternoon. He requests me to call again at his house tomorrow morning, and so as I could not find my former guide and feeling rather lost and solitary amongst such a hive out into the street and to a walk in the Park. Strolled through the Mall—so a wayfarer informed it was called—a vastly fine place and into St. James Park, where I was much edified by a fine sight of Westminster Abbey rising from the ancient trees that surround it. Dined at a tavern and so home tired to an early bed.

September 20.

Dressed myself with care this morning, powdering my hair and greasing my shoes with considerable more care than I usually bestow upon such matters, so as not to appear unworthy of my revered uncle of whom Doct. Urquehart would seem to entertain the warmest regards. To breakfast with an unwonted sense of my professional dignity, due I suspect, God forgive me, to having seen the misery of that poor wretch of a porter yesterday, and so on to Doctor Urquehart's house. Found a number of young gentlemen there amongst them my short friend of yesterday, and learn that his name is George Blumenfield, from him hear that the porter whose leg was removed yesterday is dead. Doctor Urquehart arrives to take us to the rear of the house where as I thought he has had a mighty fine dissecting room built cunningly contrived with a small door leading to a plot of waste ground adjacent to a parish graveyard. A subject already present a highwayman hanged yesterday at noon and was much relieved to find that my anatomising was to commence with such a fine fresh corpse and not with some over-ripe charnel house fruit. The Doctor commences his lectures with a discourse on the Similar and Dissimilar parts of the body, the Similar being commonly reckoned to be eleven and being those which though they be cut or divided into several pieces yet will be found to be of the same Nature, Substance and Denomination with one another and with the whole to wit The Skin, the Flesh, the Nerve and so forth, the Dissimilar being Compound or Organical bodies such as A Finger A Toe. These things I was already acquaint with and so to drowsing until the Doctor who is somewhat prosy ceased his talk and came to the body to show that of which he had spoken; and so with George Blumenfield to dissect the foot he grumbling that he had been promised the head. Doctor Urquehart calls me to one side and I pay him twenty guineas for his tuition and guidance this to include the cost of two bodies, and I consider this somewhat of an expense since though he is no doubt a Very Famous Man my uncle taught me nigh as much as I expect to learn from the Doctor for no more than to compound his draughts and elixirs.

We passed the morning in anatomising I using a knife borrowed from Mr. Blumenfield to reflect back the skin and clean the sanguineous vessels beneath it. The Doctor to the Infirmary about noon with some of the young gentlemen but requests me to stay and make myself better acquaint with the General Subject of Anatomy that most noble of subjects that I may in a day or so better appreciate the application of Surgery that beneficial end of Anatomy. So to read with Mr. Blumenfield in Gibson's Anatomy my uncle's copy, which though old is thought much of by him, Mr. Blumenfield saying that he had had a surfeit of Infirmary and Autopsies and would by my leave content himself for once with the company of the living; the which I took very kindly of him. Dined with him at the Leaping Hart and after to walk in Marylebone Gardens, very fine. Retired to bed early my mind rather in a confusion with all these new novelties.

September 21.

Sunday; with Mr. Hunt and his wife to the parish church of Marylebone, it being a fine morning the walk through the fields exceeding pleasant. Mr. Hunt points out to me the portion of the common where last week a gentleman was set upon by thieves and grievously hurt. A wearisome sermon of some hour and a quarter upon the Spiritual Elements of Man the which I beguiled may Heaven forgive me in quizzing a pretty wench who sat in the musicians gallery and led the singing with a fair sweet voice, and she proving demure, to sleep.

To walk in the Gardens in the afternoon and after supper Mr. Hunt reads prayers and so to bed.

September 22.

Was awoke last night by a vile noise of shouting to find two foxed gentlemen endeavouring to make entrance with some idea that it was an Inn. Mrs. Hunt very courageous empties slops over them on which they became vehement with rage and were only detained from entrance by Mr. Hunt firing a pistol out of the window at them; the which I took kindly of him as affording me a case of gunshot wound for treatment only they took fright and retired. So to sleep once more and Mr. Hunt very apologetic at breakfast it seeming that one of the bucks had oft been shaved by him and had returned with his companion to find sport with the Hunt's serving wench; which was sufficient proof of their drunkenness the wench being undersized pitted with the Pox and afflicted with Strabismus. So to Doctor Urqueharts to anatomise in all humility and interest, Grge. Blumenfield being absent for some reason best known to himself. I am afraid he is a sad rogue.

September 23.

Anatomised at the Doctor's house Mr. Blumenfield still being absent. In afternoon to Mr. Kelly the gentleman with the fine peruke to whom I had paid five guineas to be instructed in the Art of Vegetable and Animal Physiology. Found only one other gentleman there beside myself, he greeting me with a most strange smile. The address of Mr. Kelly very fine—Langham Chambers, Golden Square, and Golden Square itself very fine, only Langham Chambers is a suite of rooms, two of which only are occupied by Mr. Kelly, situate in a dirty house at the corner. Mr. Kelly unable for some reason to see either myself or the other gentleman; on the which I made my way into the streets and desired of my companion what manner of man Mr. Kelly was; on which he burst into laughter and said that if I would return the next week at the same time I should doubtless find for myself. In some lowness of spirit to walk through the streets to buy myself some stockings very dear at 6/— a pair and a small sword in a gilded sheath 28/— and two fine cambric shirts at 14/— each, and so home to read in my anatomy. Trust that I shall soon be thought fit to accompany the Doctor on his visits to the Infirmary.

September 24.

Arriving at the Doctor's house this morning for my lecture found George Blumenfield there with his arm in a sling and on my enquiring the reason he spoke to me with much choler asking me whether I thought it friendly to fire off powder and ball at my visitors, the which I took exception to the more so as I was hard put to it to imagine of what he spoke. After much talk find that he was one of the bucks at whom Mr. Hunt fired his pistol the evening of the 21st.; that having learnt from me of my lodging at Mr. Hunt's he had thought in all friendliness to call upon me his friend much liking the idea and assuring him that Mr. Hunt was a worthy man with a serving wench the prettiest doxy in all London; but upon their arrival they were much hurt to find themselves so barbarously treated. On hearing which I made haste to assure Mr. Blumenfield that he was fortunate to have escaped with a bullet graze only the wench aforesaid being I suspect a very repositary for all diseases from the Small to the Great Pox.

So to anatomise together with friendliness at last and dined with much liveliness at the Leaping Hart.

September 25.

This day wet and the streets very unpleasant the rain dripping off the roof gables and collecting in pools amongst the broken cobbles. To my great pleasure Doctor Urquehart after this morning's lecture confesses himself well pleased with my progress and with him and the other young gentlemen to Infirmary Hall. George Blumenfield not at the lecture but waiting for us at the porch and so with us into the wards. Doctor Urquehart at the entry changes his peruke for a tie wig and puts on a short coat as his fine full skirted one would brush the walls and sweep from them the lice and other insects which infect them. The wards at first sight rather curious; the beds of moderate width and containing not more than three to four patients, but these placed the feet of one to the head of another so that each receives not the tainted effluvium of their respective complaints. In the infants wards there were of course any from six to eight in one bed. Pregnant women have their own ward to which they are taken when the pains seize them, but from the press those in the earlier stages are frequently put to lie with those about to die, so that comfort is had by both. The air rather foul, especially in the surgical ward, which lies at the end of the great Hall where all the general cases lie, but this of course no more than can be expected since the windows cannot be allowed open. For the safety of those that minister to them it is customary for these to carry some prophylactic which can be held to the nostrils; the attendants as a rule carry a sponge soaked in vinegar and those in the Surgical room a cresset of smoking sulphur held in an iron cup at the end of an iron wand. All these things I noted later.

The Doctor had a number of operations awaiting, so with him to that room which I had visited the first day. Here I found Mr. Jamie the Infirmary surgeon and his assistant removing a wen from the shoulder of an elderly woman of great strength of character. I admired the fortitude with which she bore the first cuts and afterwards rose from the table and walked to her bed. A number of well known

Doctors and Surgeons present, I found to see my teacher attempt the removal of a broken jaw from a carrier. The man being bound and the assistants leaning their weight upon him Doctor Urquehart and a gentleman from another Hospital cut down through the Masseteric Muscle on the left side to the Mandible and endeavoured to remove the broken portion. But after some twenty minutes they had to desist as the tongue had become involved and the patient had lost about two pints of blood, and the surgeon from the other Hospital therefore bound the broken fragment with wire and the patient was removed and given instructions to keep quiet. Saw the Doctor remove a foot very neatly also a finger from a sempstress and then with him to the wards where we arrived in time to see Mr. Rickard the Infirmary Physician order the removal of a case of Rising of the Lights or Phthisica Pneumonica. So with the other gentlemen to see the autopsy on this case the Doctor proving in a merry and generous mood. The lungs riddled with exuviæ of Nature's effort to expel the morbific humours, very instructive, and so back with him to the Surgical Wards where we saw some of his patients of the previous days all of them doing well the wounds suppurating healthily. So out and it being late in the afternoon to dine lightly at a coffee house and then to walk beneath the trees in St. James Park pondering on all that I had seen and so home to supper and bed.

September 26.

To anatomise at the Doctor's house he showing us on the cadaver the manner of performing certain operations especially that most beneficent art of applying pressure to relieve hæmorrhage. The cadaver now growing rather rank and I for one thankful that the weather continues cold. A body it seems lasts for a class of our present numbers about a fortnight or a little longer and George Blumenfield assures me that it becomes in summer a task of heroic proportions to approach it at the last. After the session to dine and then to the Infirmary where the Doctor this day hands us over to Doctor Leeds for instruction in the Materia Medica and with him to compound various plasters, charges, elixirs, draughts, and clysters. Doctor Leeds the appointed instructor in Medicine and Materia Medica but has been ill this last three weeks with a low fever. Home and to bed after some reading in my Sydenham of the uses of drugs.

September 27.

Up betimes and to the Infirmary direct the Doctor having requested us this day to go there direct. With Mr. Rickard to the wards and to assist him. My attention catched by an old man his face very weather beaten, "Belloque Fractorum" to wit his old body shattered by much fighting with the Spaniards and French. Did talk with him awhile improving my skill by taking his pulse this very slow and weak and soft from his age but the more so from his heart, that Fount of the Vital Spirits, having been injured by a pike thrust in the chest received some three years since but from which that organ has never recovered. Mr. Rickard informs me that on his first entry to the Infirmary three months gone he did bleed him some three ounces twice daily, but this having but small effect in lightening the work of his heart he had desisted and the old man was now awaiting the call of the Last Muster in all humbleness and Christian resignation, passing his days in converse with another old man in the same bed. I took this kindly of Mr. Rickard for such cases I learn are usually sent to a poor-house to die, but he with a smile informs me that the ancient mariner had hitherto payed a small sum to be allowed to stay there with his friend; but that this was now exhausted so that he would have to be put out into the street to die. The old man very feeble and reminded me of a favorite spannell dog I left at home, not wishing me to go and asking me very cringing whether I would call to see him on the morrow; which I promised him to do.

Leaving the Infirmary passed the bed of the carter with the fractured mandible; he now far gone in a Hectic Fever so that they had tied him to the bed and the assistant was applying Hippocrates His Heroic Treatment, the which is bleeding the patient upright till he faints then laying him down till he recovers and then seating him upright and bleeding him till he faints again; the which desperate course though rigorous is necessitated by the quantity of effete matter rioting in the Sanguineous System and oppressing the Vital Members.

September 28.

This morning overslept for some reason and to breakfast in something of a hurry. With Mr. Hunt and his wife to Church walking through the fields. To my disappointment the wench of last week not present in the choir and do wonder whether His Reverence is responsible for this he preaching a very heated sermon on the Lusts of the Flesh and the Seven Deadly Sins his eye catching mine most extraordinary several times so that I scarce dared to compose myself for sleep, though I needed it the Church being very stuffy. Walked in the Gardens afterwards, and to bed early.

September 29.

Woke this morning with a full head and on taking my pulse found it somewhat rapid; have perhaps catched a rheum. Had no appetite for my breakfast the which was unusual enough to make Mrs. Hunt enquire anxiously after my health. To Doctor Urqueharts and after dinner to the Infirmary, where I assisted in divers ways. Visited the old sailor whose name I discover to be Ned Jackson and to Mr.

Rickard to whom I entrust enough of money to ensure that the worthy Ned shall not be turned out into the street, and a little also to buy him and his friend a few of those creature comforts that mean so much to the penniless aged. To bed with a shocking headache.

II

October 11.

Have been very sick this last fortnight with a low fever contracted I doubt not from the night air of the town whilst I sat at this Journal before retiring, the which I am resolved never to do more but to write it by the light of the supper candles after that repast is ended. It seems that the morning following my last entry Mr. Hunt finds I do not rise on calling and on entry finds me light-headed and very feverish and on my persistence the worthy man sends his wife to fetch Doctor Urquehart who comes at noon with George Blumenfield now without doubt my friend for Mr. Hunt informs me that he has not missed a day in calling and has sat by my bed wiping the sweat from me and moistening my lips; the which I am humbly grateful to Almighty God for sending me a stranger amongst such friends in the hour of my need. It needs no discernment on my part to see that I would likely have died had it not been for the ministrations of my excellent host and hostess, aye and even of that smutty service wench of whom may God forgive me I have spoken so lightly and who is a wholesome lesson to me of what good wine may lodge in a dirty flask. No more tonight as my hand is weak and writing tires me.

October 12.

Still very weak; lay abed till after noon, listening to the church-bells.

October 13.

A nasty day with a mist and drizzling rain. Again could not stir from my room for fear of catching a distemper. Doctor Urquehart to call on me in the afternoon and pronounces me now whole and well, saying jovially that I was fortunate to be in my bed and not stark on his anatomy table, he having a view that I would make a fine specimen being by God's grace and my father's care a lusty youth. It seems that he at one time feared for my life, but by bleeding and throwing up the Peruvian Bark my fever did slowly abate and so I came to health again. In the evening George Blumenfield to see me with two of his friends and I to thanking him very heartily for all his compassion to me. This he laughs aside and his friend producing a mandoline to a very pleasant hour of music, Mr. Hunt to join us, and the other friend of Mr. Blumenfield proving to have a most dulcet and sympathetic voice at the singing of catches and ballads. They have but this moment left me and as I finish this I will to my knees to thank My Almighty Father for all His care and thought for me in sending me such pleasant companions in this my sojourn in our great city.

October 14.

This day the rain having abated and the day being tolerably warm and dry for the season of year ventured to walk for an hour in the afternoon in the fields adjacent to this house, admiring the quaint old house in the square which I am told dates from the days of Her Majesty Elizabeth, when these fields did resound to the cries of the rabbit hunters So-Ho! So-Ho! this gaining this rus-in-urbe its present title of Soho.

October 15.

Ventured to rise this morning to take my breakfast with the Hunts in their breakfast room and feeling now quite well again to Doctor Urqueharts to take up once more my Anatomy. George Blumenfield there with the two young gentlemen that visited me with him; their names are respectively Thomas Pope and Henry Augustus St. Clair and are a contrast in that both are slim and tall but Mr. Pope is dark and St. Clair despite his name a bucolic looking fellow with a snub nose, red face, and yellow hair that he ties in a que behind he complaining that no wig can be found to suit him; the which I can readily believe. Doctor Urquehart very pleasant and to enquire after my health and so with him and my friends and the other gentlemen of the class who have increased in numbers during my absence to Infirmary Hall where I was put to the Pharmacy to assist Doctor Leeds in the dispensing. To see my friend the sailor Ned whom I found in tolerable health and so home early.

October 18.

Have not written in my journal these few days there being no chance of writing after supper as on my return home the worthy Mrs. Hunt always bustles me into bed to take my supper there. I verily believe the good woman quite comes to look upon me as her son.

October 20.

The serving wench returned to her home this day her mother being grievously ill with a strangury. Did give her a shilling for serving me and a crown for looking after me when I was sick; on the which the wench to my astonishment bursts out crying. Do not believe that she has ever received so much money from a chance stranger before. At the infirmary did see a very pretty cutting for the stone performed by one William Hunter a well known Anatomist and Natural Philosopher of whom Doctor Urquehart speaks very highly.

October 21.

This day to dissect the arm a new body having been obtained from the authorities, and to a lecture by Doctor Leeds.

October 22.

Was reminded this day of my five guineas paid to Mr. Kelly for a course in Vegetable and Animal Physiology and to Golden Square vowing to camp on the stairs were the gentleman not at home. But on climbing the stairs and knocking at his door was admitted by a hard-faced slattern unlaced and her bosom exposed who informed me with contempt that Mr. Kelly was at home and so to his chamber where I found him in a dressing gown, his wig off and his bald crown marked with flea-bites, he seated at a table by the window at a Monstrous fine Microscope; the which I recognized from having heard my uncle speak of an Italian Anatomist Marcello Malphigi who had applied its principle to unravel the Structure of the Human Frame.

Mr. Kelly to his feet and to asking very courteously after my health and the reason for this my visit; on which I remind him of my five guineas paid for Instruction. He then informs me that the next class meets on the morrow in the evening but on seeing perhaps the doubt in my face says that he will give me Instruction then and now if I can afford the time on which methought that there is no time like

The Dissecting Room

The figure standing up above the rest is William Hunter. His brother John is at his right.

(AFTER ROWLANDSON)

the present and so to agree, and to take a seat at the table before the Microscope. This machine a Fine one nigh two feet high and all scrolls and inlaid work which Mr. Kelly informs me was specially made for him by Benjamin Martin. He then to inform me that this Instrument is the only True Teacher of Truth; the which I found it hard to believe but I learn then that its Mechanicks have revealed the Structure of Animals and Plants to be of a Vastly different Nature to that supposed by the Ancients, that one Hooke found Vegetables to be built of little boxes and that Malphigi and others with it found the Body of both animals and Man to be built of fibres and tubes of a Complexity the most confusing. Mr. Kelly then to show me a drop of Water taken from his gutter the which swarmed with invisible tiny animals or Animalculæ whose antics I found vastly diverting, and he to inform me that such creatures did swarm even within the Noble Temple of Man especially within Tumours and the Like where they were generated from the Heat and Decomposition of the Flesh. He informs me likewise that the Purple Tide of Life the Blood contains globules that can be seen to roll through Vessels finer than the tiniest hair; and to ask him in much perplexity the use of these globules, when our discourse interrupted by the Slattern, who brings Mr. Kelly's wig to the table and asks him whether he is not ashamed to be seen without it and whether he is not thoughtless to keep a young gentleman from his proper studies; on which seeing that she grew violent I withdrew and to the Infirmary pondering on the Strange Power and Wisdom of God as revealed through Nature.

October 24.

Was late to bed last night and so no entry in my journal my mind being moreover in great confusion. After attendance at Infirmary Hall did repair in the evening once more to Mr. Kelly's chambers there to hear the lecture of which he spoke. The slattern to my comfort absent, and several gentlemen present, amongst whom I recognised the young buck met there previous and two other members of Doctor Urquehart's class. Mr. Kelly with reference to me says that he will demonstrate the Circulation of the Globules of the Blood and so to take a frog and spread its toe web out upon the bridge or landing of his Microscope; and then after much squinting and turning of a great Mirror we all to have a gaze and I for one greatly marvelled to see oval corpuscles tumbling like rocks over a waterfall in channels that try as I might I could not see with my Unaided Eye. And so to be shown The Animalculæ in the Semine Masculino, and I for one near foxed to gather reason for these things which must of necessity have a use and yet of which were it not for this Magic Toy we should have no knowledge. One fat jovial gentleman an Apothecary then to quiz Mr. Kelly on whether he has found the cause of Disease yet, Mr. Kelly holding that Disease visits us from without and is not an expression of Lack or Excess of one of the Vital Humours, as was held I learn by the ancients for example one Tarentius Varro who supposed the air of marshes harmful because of animalculæ contained in it. But Lord such matters strike deep; did not our Blessed Lord say that it is those things that go out of a man that defile him? Left Mr. Kelly's chambers late, at eleven of the clock, with one of Doctor Urquehart's gentlemen, and was mighty glad of his company. For on the road we did meet a gang of Tumblers putting a woman in a barrel and then with great laughter and noise setting her to roll down the street the Watch interfering and being severely beaten for his pains. So home by another way very tired and muddy from the roads. Have this day attended to my Anatomising and Infirmary.

October 26.

This day being Sunday to Church with Mr. Hunt and wife. Hear that the choir wench has died in child-bed, this greatly astonishing me, till I learn that she was only five months gone but was frighted by a gang of Mohawks a week back.

October 27.

At Doctor Urqueharts this morning to complete my dissecting of the arm. Made a preparation of the sinews of the wrist now varnishing.

October 29.

Have led a sober life these two days my mind still being greatly exercised by what Mr. Kelly has shown me. Am half resolved to let my five guineas go this being a small price to pay if I can preserve My Tranquillity of Spirits.

October 30.

Dissected the shoulder and so to finish my arm.

November 4.

This day George Blumenfield and I to see a hanging at Tyburn of a woman who stole three loaves. Was ready enough for some diversion for have kept close to my business these last days and the stench of the Infirmary though one grows accustomed to it is tiresome for long times. Doctor Urquehart himself though pompous has a real mind to the Instruction of his pupils and had kindly taken seats in a nearby house for self, Grge. Blumenfield, St. Clair, Mr. Pope and three other of his young gentlemen. On taking our seats found a crowd already gathered such occasions being quite a holiday for the poor people who live in Oxford Street, and also for those in the villages of Paddington and the hamlets along the road leading to Edgeware. A number of the gentry present, standing on the roofs of their coaches both the gentlemen and the ladies very fine, the bucks dressing as for a route and the ladies all powdered and patched, monstrous pretty with their scarves and great hats and flowered pannier skirts.

The gallows a big one to take four at once but this day only the woman to be hanged, and with her a boy who is to be half-hanged and then cut down and whipped through the town as a warning to him against begging. George Blumenfield very merry and quizzing the ladies on the coaches and Mr. Pope kindly sends out to a drawer for cans of liquor for us all, which puts us quite happy to watch the Turning Off. The woman arrives after we had waited some twenty minutes a young wench not ill-favoured, driven in a cart tied on to a board so that she might not leap over the side; the hangman greeting her with much cheer and she answering him in kind, so that the crowd and the gentry were Highly Diverted, one buck near me with a vast wig I thought would swoon with mirth, and so she to the Tree and the hangman makes her mount upon a bucket, she being a Vagabond and of no importance, and then fastens the rope about her neck and she blowing him a kiss his assistant pulls away the bucket and she fell with a force that must instantly have deprived her of Her Vital Faculties. Was intrigued to see how the body did jerk so that I thought the rope would break. Then the boy aforesaid, who had been brought there very early so that the execution might prove of instruction to him, was taken up, he squalling in a fashion that made the gentry cry Shame upon His Cowardice, and proving near frantic the hangman did not trouble to tie him to the tree but threw him to the ground and encouraged by shouts from the crowd did kneel upon his chest and strangle him with a cord, removing same before the boy was dead. Then the rogue was pulled to his feet and a bucket of water splashed over him, and so he was taken to the cart in which the woman came and tied to its tail two gentlemen nigh our window shouting themselves hoarse with admiration; and the hangman's assistant takes up his whip and the cart moves on the assistant wielding the rope right shrewdly. The woman was cut down and delivered to her father who had been waiting for her corse with a barrow, and so the crowd disperses and the gentry drive off one lady laying her whip about the ears of the father with his barrow for not being out of the road of her coach. And so to dine with my friends and a very pleasant hour of music and talk afterwards on divers topics. Did learn that the woman hanged was the mother of the boy aforesaid which I trust will be a lesson to him of the Penalties of An Evil Life.

November 5.

Anatomised at Doctor Urqueharts and to the Infirmary where I did hear a merry tale of two bucks and their friends who to commemorate the disclosure of Guido Fawkes his Vile Plot did set upon a watchman and burn his hut about his ears so that the worthy was roasted and is like to die.

November 7.

On arriving at Doctor Urqueharts this day did find my worthy teacher in a great choler and learn from Mr. Blumenfield that he has been disappointed in getting the body of the woman we saw hanged for Anatomising, the which is sad news for us all, as the last body is nigh finished. She has been buried nearby in the parish graveyard. My sailor friend the worthy Ned not so well this morning and I fear that he nears the End of His Last Voyage and so to comfort him and to bleed him with one of the lancets my uncle did give me they proving to my great satisfaction as sharp and keen as they are comely.

November 9.

Vastly tired this morning as a result of a Hazardous Escapade from which I count myself lucky to have escaped without Grievous Harm to Life and Limb. Mr. Blumenfield did yester eve put to me that we should disinter the body of the hanged woman for the Advancement of Our Art and the Glory of Medicine and so after some talk I agreed and we approached our worthy teacher who warning us of the Dangers—for hanging is not the least penalty, one is likely to be torn to pieces by the mob should they learn of it—did then commend our Diligence and whilst saying that he would have no hand in it and would know nothing of it should it come to light, did call his huge manservant to him and gave him instructions that he was to help us. So home to an early supper and to acquaint Mr. Hunt that that night I was to a meeting of Physicians and because of the dangers of the streets would after lie at the house of a friend, this because I thought it imprudent to return home mired in the early dawn. Then to take up my small sword and so to Doctor Urqueharts to enter it by the small gate to find the Doctor gone out but his man and George Blumenfield and Messrs. Pope and St. Clair gathered in the Anatomy room very comfortable before a fire smoking and discussing a flask of wine, and they very merry at my sword. So with them to pass the evening in pleasant discourse I growing somewhat drunk on the wine, very potent; and when the clocks had struck the half after twelve to collect spades and grapples and to muffle ourselves in thick cloaks.

I was given a spade but betwixt the Wine and the Excitement of My Spirits did so catch it in my cloak that Doctor Urquehart's man did take it from me and give me the sack in which they carry the bodies this having a most foul and dismal charnel house odour. And so into the lane and to the graveyard where Mr. Pope was inspired to Belch loudly this causing Doctor Urquehart's man to swear vilely vowing that he would rather have a School of Apes to help him than such young turnip heads. The grave not easy to find there being very many in a small place and the moon did come out from behind the clouds the which I did not care for as we were more likely to be seen but with its aid to find where the mould had been newly turned. George Blumenfield very vehement to dig up the coffin only this on being opened did prove to contain an old woman very foul and I to pray with all my heart that Venus Cloacina the Goddess of Sewers would watch over us this night so that we caught not some enervating distemper; then Mr. St. Clair on sitting down did find the ground give way beneath him and so we found the hanged wench and dragged her out and put into the sack which Mr. Pope and I did then carry between us and with great haste to the lane and so to the Doctors again, all mired and sweaty. George Blumenfield did brew us a bowl of punch and we certainly in need of such a Specific. Lord, what a business this be, this Quickening of the Aweful Dead, at night when the powers of evil be abroad, amongst the tombs and the earth and the dreadful worms! Fit work only for men of Brutish Minds! Did resolve then to have no more of it, but on reflection realise that nothing is gained without labour and so as Medicine be the most noble of the Arts so the Gateway to it is correspondingly difficult and arduous to pass. Slept on a couch at the Doctor's, and so home this morning to Mr. Hunt's, and with him and Mrs. Hunt to church, where I heard a tolerable Sermon aptly enough on the Resurrection, and wonder what his Reverence would say of my night's activities. Shall to bed early this night.

III

November 10.

At Doctor Urqueharts this morning to draw lots as to the disposal of the body of the hanged woman, and to my satisfaction George Blumenfield and I did get the head, and Mr. Pope and Mr. St. Clair did take the trunk. The other gentlemen of the class to content themselves with the limbs, and on one enquiring where the body came from Mr. Blumenfield did tell him that it was Spontaneously Generated from a cow dropping outside our door. And so he and I to dissect the head this proving vastly interesting especially the neck where we did trace the Injuries caused by her Hanging, finding that the Odontoid Process of the Second Cervical Vertebra had torn its ligaments and pulled away from its junction with the Atlas so bruising the Spinal Cord that this was shattered and the Animal Spirits which flow from the Brain dissipated. Doctor Urquehart much pleased with us and did say that it was Good to have a female to dissect as he would then be able next month to send us to Mr. Rickard for Instruction in Midwifery.

November 12.

Have been busy these two days at the Infirmary and Anatomising.

November 14.

To Mr. Kelly's room to hear his latest lecture, not having been this last fortnight. He did give me and two other gentlemen an interesting talk on the structure of the Vegetable; but I can see that his talks are not likely to be of use to me as a Surgeon the rascal gathering his guineas from young green fellows such as I was to pay for his room and his board and his Magic Glasses. Did learn however that he is a Fellow of the Royal Society the which is something to tell my uncle should he ever enquire into my accompts; the which may God forbid.

November 15.

The old sailor Ned Jackson died this day. Did arrive at Infirmary Hall this midday to find him far gone, speechless and plucking at the bedclothes, the old man his friend crying and smoothing his hand. Did for my instruction try to rally him with hartshorn and feathers burnt beneath his nostrils but with no effect; his pulse grew so soft and small that I at last lost it completely and then saw that the facies Hippocratica had appeared and so without struggle he gives up His Spirit. The old man in the same bed with him crying bitterly now that he has lost his friend, and I to comfort him and may God forgive me to assume the role of parson and to tell him to look up to Him who never forgets the Aged and Helpless; and thereby to ask Mr. Rickard to devote what is left of my monies given to him to keep Ned to this old man. The nurse that attends their room, a fat blowsy old bitch, for once sober and to my relief removes Ned without her usual Coarse Remarks.

November 16.

At church.

November 21.

Very busy these days with my anatomising of the hanged woman's head, vastly interesting. Did this day expose the Pineal Body or Gland that Organ which Descartes I am informed considered the Seat of the Soul; on which to wondering what Mr. Kelly might see in it with his Microscope.

November 23.

On leaving church today with Mr. and Mrs. Hunt the parson approached us and with many smiles said that he was pleased to observe my diligence in Church Observance and would be glad if I would take supper with him during the coming week; to which I agreed. Am to go there next Wednesday at five of the clock.

November 25.

Assisted Doctor Urquehart with an Amputation of the leg, and the removal of a breast from an aged woman afflicted with a Cancer. The leg was taken from an attorney's clerk who had broken it coming down some dark stairs in the Temple late one night. The tibia whole but the fibula broken some three or four inches above the ancle joint and protruding through the skin, the ancle itself dislocated. The clerk in great pain and the wound discharging through part of his black stocking having been caught by the bone and drawn into the wound. The wound about the exit of the bone very foul the flesh about swollen and the skin hard and shiny to half-way up the shin; so that the Doctor did resolve to remove the leg at the knee. The clerk was taken from his bed in Great Lowness of Spirits his wife being with him and comforting him and attempting to follow him into the Theatre; from which she was prevented by Doctor Urquehart's man who at a sign from him did pick her up bodily and carry her to the gates, where she was attended by one of the nurses. Then the clerk being bound his leg was held out firmly by the aforesaid servant who wedged it against his belly and Doctor Urquehart with a sharp knife cuts a half-circle from below the Tubercle of the Tibia to the middle of the joint behind and repeats same on the opposing side and I pull these flaps back and get soaked with blood from the great arteries at which the Doctor laughs. Then he severs the Ligamentum Patellæ and the other ligaments and cuts through the cartilages so that the leg drops to the floor, he leaving the Semilunar Cartilages in place so that they may form a protection for the Condyles of the Femur and prevent its retraction, and then he ligatures the Vessels with cords and sews up the two flaps leaving the ends of the ligature cords hanging from the wound. The Doctor a very quick man and the leg off in four minutes, though due to my clumsiness another minute or two elapsed before the wound was secured. I have heard and can well believe that when he Amputates with another cunning and experienced surgeon only two or three minutes elapse before it is complete. And so the clerk was removed in all Peace he having fainted from the Vehemence of His Emotions at the cutting of the second flap and I for one very thankful, for his screams at the first nigh deafened me.

Then to remove the old woman's breast she walking in on the arm of a fat nurse and Doctor Urquehart greeting her with much cheer. Did not see the reason for removal of the breast the old woman being I should imagine about sixty years of age and likely to die shortly, but must bow to the Superior Knowledge of my Teacher. The Doctor very quick again; it was not necessary to bind such a frail creature and so his man servant holding her down with an arm round her throat he did pinch up the shrivelled flesh and with one sweeping cut remove not only the growth and the breast but half the skin adjacent, and then sprinkles the wound with Powdered Galls to discourage the further Growth of the Tumour. A third case being brought in with a Great Ulcer on the Sole of the Left Foot the Doctor resolves to remove the foot and so the patient a beggar bound to the table and Doctor Urquehart cuts through the bones of the Ancle in such manner that the stump of the heel is left about the Os Calcis, and the beggar being a lusty full-blooded wight much blood was shed. At the termination of this operation the beggar confesses to having a further Ulcer on the groin of that same side and Doctor Urquehart in a great Passion saying that the man had like got the French Disease and if so would burst with Ulcers till he died his labour in taking off the foot going for naught.

So home very sweaty and bloody to change my shirt and cravat.

November 26.

To Supper with his Reverence, Mr. Hardy. An infernally dull evening though Mr. Hardy a well meaning man enough. Do not like his wife, a shrew; did not offer me a second helping of meat pie, and only lemonade to drink.

November 27.

To Mr. Kelly's again, having learnt that he would be at his rooms today. A very intriguing discourse on the structure of the Human Frame as revealed by the Microscope but could not understand the half of it. He did speak also of a Ladder of Nature, quoting one Baker, His *Microscope Made Easy,* of how the whole Chasm from a Plant to a Man, is filled up with divers kinds of creatures, rising one over another by such a gentle and easy ascent, that the little Transitions and Deviations from one Species to another are almost insensible so that the Scale of Life rising by degrees to such a one as Man we may equally suppose that it still proceeds upwards through numberless beings of an order superior to him to the Throne of the Father of all; to the which idea I did take very kindly and was pleased for once to find Mr. Kelly's philosophy and mine so well agree; having wondered a little whether his microscope may not a little have addled his wits so that he approaches the unreasoning state of the savage.

Coming home did see a troupe of Sweaters at work these surrounding two poor wights and prodding them with their swords to make them dance, and did halt undecided which way to turn and so they did see me and I to my heels and lose myself in a very ill quarter of the town from which I made equal speed to free myself and so by asking a Watchman the way, to my lodgings at last very fatigued, and muddied from head to toe with the dirt of the roads. Will always after this carry my sword.

November 30.

At my anatomising these days and my knowledge and skill praise to God grows apace. Very wet and foggy, but to church by the roads, Mr. Hunt and wife and self joining three neighbours for greater safety.

December 1.

At the Infirmary this day did get a fine prescription against the Asthma, to wit:

℞

Take Syrup of Maidenhair and Horehound, of each three ounces; Balsam of Sulphur made with oil of Turpentine 20 drops; Black cherry water, the greater Compound Wormwood Water, Tincture of Saffron prepared with Sack, of each four ounces; mix and take three spoonfuls every morning and at pleasure, when the breathing is troublesome.

This Doctor Leeds says is a Specific; for Asthmas depending upon a want of Spirits; then such a cordial by adding vigour enables the costæ to raise their load the Lungs or Lights to greater height and so relieve the Asthma. Moreover in such cases where the blood has become overcharged and the spirits become evaporated or oppressed, as seen in Debauchees, such a Julep will invigorate and reinstate the Spirits.

The clerk with the Amputated leg doing well his fever light. Did remove the ligatures about the Great Vessels by gentle twitching this under the instruction of Doctor Urquehart these not having sloughed out as usual. God being all merciful no hæmorrhage followed. The old dame with the cancerous breast died yesterday and an autopsy revealed her body to be riddled with the Metastases of the growths. The beggar also doing well but Doctor Urquehart would have no more of him and so left to the ministrations of Mr. Jamie and self.

December 2.

My dissection of the woman's head finished and desiring to have a memento did with George Blumenfield boil it to obtain the skull. This done and now waiting for the flesh still within to separate.

December 3.

The clerk doing well. Today to watch George Blumenfield assist Doctor Urquehart at the operations. Dined with him at the Leaping Hart.

December 5.

Doctor Urquehart obtained a fresh body for us, that of a man found dead in the streets. Did pay him a guinea and gained the trunk for anatomising.

December 6.

This day at the Infirmary did see a remarkable thing. George Blumenfield and I and another gentleman to assist Mr. Jamie with a man with a Scrotal

Hernia Mr. Jamie having decided to cut for it. The man being brought in and held in the correct Posture Mr. Blumenfield did proceed to throw up a Tobacco-Water Clyster to empty the bowel and make our work the easier and the safer for our patient. But as he ceased the clyster did work with much force, there was a Loud Rumble and the hernia did vanish! at the which we all marvelled. Mr. Jamie therefore did pass a seton to close the Path of the Hernia that the Inflammation might bind its walls together.

In the afternoon I and Messrs. Blumenfield, Pope and St. Clair together with some other young gentlemen of Doctor Urquehart's class to Mr. Rickard for instruction in the Diseases of Women especially appertaining to Child-bed and he did show us divers preparations to this end. There is still much prejudice I learn against the Interference of Surgeons in Child Bearing despite the work of that most excellent School of Midwifery founded by the Scots at Glasgow. Women are strange creatures as has been known from the days of the Ancients. They still prefer the ministrations of some Poxy old Harridan and to have their brats in their own homes amongst a mob of squalling sister neighbours, saying that these our Hospitals are as the Jaws of Hell to swallow them up. But Lord how can some dirty fuddled Mid-Wife possess that knowledge of Anatomy without which the Art becomes a mere Empiric? And speak-

An Early Blood-Transfusion

(FROM SCULTITUS)

ing at least for this my School the patients are well cared for; the sheets on the beds are changed once a fortnight and their night rails once in a week, when there are enough of these for this to be done; and the floors are washed at least once in a month or so. But efforts for the common weal are ever carried out against the Opposition of the Ignorant who mistake vehement abuse for Reasoned Criticism.

December 7.

At church. Some gentry drove over in their coaches from their houses at Marylebone very fine.

December 11.

Late home last night from an evening with my three friends. At the Infirmary in the afternoon Mr. Rickard did speak to us of Version or The Turning of the Child at Parturition and showed us the Forceps used to this end, these being made after a pattern designed by one Jean Palfyne, but modified by Dr. Smellie. Then we four feeling in the mood for Levity did wander through the streets entering the City by the gates at Ludgate and so into that Road called the Fleet Street a very famous road the haunt of both wits and roues. We entered The Devils Tavern which is the Second house and a great resort of Physicians many meeting here for pleasant philosophical discourse, to find it very crowded many people coming and going. On enquiring the reason of the Host he did inform us that that night one Johnson a famous novelist known to his friends as the Doctor was giving a dinner in honour of a Mrs. Lennox who had published her first novel "The Life of Harriet Stuart," he and the members of his club coming there from their usual meeting place in Ivy Lane Paternoster Row. We were therefore uncertain whether we might stay as some score of guests were expected and it seemed likely that there would be no room for us. George Blumenfield however did catch sight of one Doctor Bathurst then entering and he knowing him to introduce us; and as we talked a monstrous fat man afflicted with a dropsy and with a great broad face comes in with a lady on his arm. He bids Doctor Bathurst good evening in a voice sonorous though pleasant and smiling round on us did ask whether we were perhaps relations of the Doctor; the which the Doctor did deny. "Then sirs," said the fat man, "ye are brothers with him in the search for knowledge?" to which Grge. Blumenfield replies that we are Surgeons in Embryo formed but not Delivered, at the which the fat man laughs and further enquiring our business does then bid us to join his gathering; the which I took kindly of him, and so we to agree, and he presents the lady to us she being we learn that Mrs. Lennox of whom the worthy landlord had spoken; and he, Dr. Bathurst informs us in a whisper, the great Johnson himself. And so in agreeable converse we went upstairs and into a large upper room very gay with many candles on a great table and the Doctor received with shouts of acclamation from some gentlemen drinking wine before a great fire of logs. Doctor Bathurst introduces us to other physicians, Doctor Barker a young man, and Doctor William M'Ghie an older man of whom I have heard Dr. Leeds speak. Doctor Bathurst very pleasant and informs us that we are fortunate indeed to have been admitted into such a company, for Johnson's Club is the most famous in London town and likely long to be remembered, the Doctor now engaged upon a great dictionary and already notable from having published a poem The Vanity of Human Wishes of which even His Majesty has well-spoken, and a Magazine the Rambler, which is published twice weekly. (Mem. To obtain copy of same) as well as various other works to wit a "Life" of his friend Richard Savage.

The Doctor was established in a great chair at the head of the table and the gentlemen all grouped themselves along it, Mrs. Lennox being seated at his right hand in a chair that with a pleasant conceit the Doctor had caused to be draped with Regal Purple, and we four found ourselves chairs at the end of the table, my seat being near the door and thereby intolerably draughty but of satisfaction since it afforded me a good view of the Doctor.

Did note that the centre piece of the table was a leather bound book surmounting a pile of fruit and laurel leaves, the which book I took to be the novel of Mrs. Lennox, later finding that this was so. The Doctor being seated did call for silence and then pouring a glass of wine say that his Physician had forbidden him wine but that in honour of the occasion he would dare to take a preparatory glass both for the good of his Digestion and for the Honour of the Lady who sat by him; and then helped by Doctor M'Ghie and one Hawkins an attorney he did rise to his feet and Tender to the Lady His Very Humble Admiration, holding out the glass to her and bowing with his shoulders and head; at which all the gentlemen rose to their feet toasting the lady with many warm little speeches of respectful admiration, she blushing and laughing and crying all at once. Then they seated themselves again and the waiters did bring in the supper, such a mighty profusion of dishes as I have never seen before, the company being a large one of some twenty souls or more and the Occasion an Important one. Amongst those dishes that I remember were:

A dish of rabbits all smothered with onions.

A leg of mutton boiled with capers and served with walnuts and melted butter.

A side of beef with frizzled potatoes.

A roasted goose and some chickens and other game.

A roasted lobster, served very cunning with all his claws arranged as though alive.

A dish of fish with their bellies stuffed with pudding.

And a current pudding and a Vast Apple Pie, this last especially ordered by the Doctor, who growing merry did wish to adorn it with Bay Leaves as a compliment to Mrs. Lennox who is a Poetess. But she laughingly demurring that they might spoil the flavour of the Pie, he to produce a crown of Laurel Leaves that he had had prepared and with this to crown her, the company all crying out and laughing at this pretty conceit. I did for once wish myself other than a Surgeon, to wit An Artist, for she made a most entrancing and ravishing picture in the candle-light, which was reflected in the softness of her pretty eyes and glinted from the jewels at her bosom.

We did drink Wine and Ale according to our taste with the Meat but the Doctor kept to Lemonade which though a foully sharp beverage did not seem to sharpen his temper. About eleven of the clock the remnants of the food were cleared away and nuts and fruit set out and coffee served; some of the gentlemen left being overcome with the Heat of the room and the potency of the Wines. I did feel somewhat foxed myself and on looking round did see that Mr. St. Clair was leaving and that Mr. Pope had already left; but did later find him beneath the table. The Doctor our host had eaten I do believe more than any one else in the room; I did marvel at the way he crammed all manner of meats into his mouth until his face became purple and the veins stood out at his Temples; but he seemed to suffer no inconvenience from it, his face now shining with sweat and merriment until it resembled a Full Moon. Moreover he never ceased talking and the flow of his discourse flowed on like a river the sonorous timbre of his voice drowning all who interrupted him. He has had I understand a rather unhappy life hitherto and likes nothing better now than to be in the thick of some discussion preferably acrimonious in the company of sundry friends and acquaintances. In reply to some remark I heard him say "Sir, I have said before and I now repeat, that the Great Chair of a full and pleasant town club is perhaps the Throne of Human felicity" the which tolerably explains his tastes. His voice did lull me to sleep and I drowsed until awoke by a prod from George Blumenfield to find Mrs. Lennox leaving with her husband, so in haste to my feet. I did lose them again as the door closed after her, and falling beneath the table did there find Mr. Pope sleeping as calm as in his bed at home, in company with sundry other gentlemen.

So to my feet again and to take a cup of Coffee which Arabian drink did clear my head so that I could listen with intelligence to a heated argument now begun between the Doctor and Mr. Payne a bookseller on the Value of Chastity in a Woman. Mr. Payne did seemingly hold it a thing of small account, but the Doctor flew into a passion declaring that of all Jewels it was the most to be prized; man being a weak creature of Gross Appetites, and only to be kept from whoring by the Decent Carriage of his Loved one, be she Sweetheart or Wife. "There is that in a man, Sir," he thundered, "which will answer to all that which is base; there is that also God be thanked which will respond to that which is Highest; and man is so made imperfect without Woman that the best in him is developed by the best in her. Chastity therefore in a woman must always be respected by you if not for yourself then for the sake of the man who may follow." Mr. Payne replies that this may be so but that it is to his mind beside the point; he being convinced from the multitude of Whores and the readiness with which a woman will become a Man's Mistress that women set no value upon chastity, whereupon the Doctor with a loud neighing laugh cries "Sir, your Logic is as faulty as your Morals! Whores have become such through one of two causes; Disease, either bodily or mental or they have become seduced at an early age when their Emotions are in a tender state" and appeals to Doctor M'Ghie for confirmation of this; and receiving it turns again to Mr. Payne and says that "A woman becoming a Man's Mistress is no proof that she belittles her chastity; rather that she loves that man above all others. The Maternal Instinct Sir is the Ruling Passion and guide in a woman; she must have a man that she can cosset and dream of as the Father of her Children. Man is imperfect without woman; that to me Sir is the meaning of Our Lord's statement that it is not good for man to live alone; and equally is it true that Woman is Imperfect without a man. As a Lock without a Key Sir so is Woman without a Man" and more to the same effect, at which I marvelled somewhat, seeing that the Doctor has married a woman who is far from a Solance and Strength.

Then about one o'clock they began discussing the Value of Health as an Aid to Morals and soared into classical dissertations far beyond the reach of My poor brain; and so feeling infernally sleepy and fuddled did awake George Blumenfield who had gone to sleep with his feet on the table and out with him into the Street. The Inn all dark mine host and his servants all gone to bed, and so home to our own beds with speed, for fear of the Night Hawks that do infest the streets at these hours. When awoke by the serving wench this morning did tell her that I would to sleep again, and to slumber till Noon, when I rose and dressed and after dining with the Hunts to Infirmary Hall; where I heard from Mr. Pope that the supper party lasted until the dawn, when the Doctor was still In Full Cry but the company much diminished and those present with difficulty keeping their feet and their wits; that more coffee was then served but that it was with difficulty that the servants could be roused and two more hours elapsed before the reckoning could be got, so that it was eight in the morning when the last guest left; at which news I was thankful that I had got me home when I did.

December 13.

Dissected the trunk this morning and was greatly edified to find the Guts full of Worms. At Infirmary Hall the clerk doing well, the beggar now coming out with boils; so to bleed him and blister him on the chest and belly.

December 14.

Snowing, with a bitter wind. Mem. Must buy myself a warm cloak.

December 15.

Mr. Rickard did finish his lectures on Midwifery and with him and the other gentlemen to the Lying-In Ward, where we did see him deliver a woman after Three Hours. He did warn us against the use of the Forceps, saying that useful as these are they are to be used only in extremis; we must trust always in the Vis Medicatrix Naturæ.

December 17.

To assist Doctor Urquehart in cutting a man for the Stone, he being brought into the Theatre tolerably fuddled with drink brought him by sundry friends; so that on our cutting him and the Doctor introducing his finger and seizing the Stone he did start to bawl and halloo "What are you at my boys? Pull away my hearties; go on, pull away!" at the which even the dry Doctor did smile faintly and I near dropped the towels and Forceps with suppressed laughter.

December 18.

Dissected, removing the heart for further work, and then with my friends to the Hall. The mother and child delivered Monday progressing well, also the worthy man cut for the Stone yesterday. The clerk's leg granulating nicely, much of the inflammation subsiding, his wife to visit him and I able to assure her that Her Good Man was now out of danger. The beggar not so well, but by reason of the Poisons circulating within him becoming tormented in the head with strange dreams and Visions; the which symptom neither Mr. Jamie or Mr. Rickard cared for. So to the Pharmacy and there to prepare a Strong Cathartic, to wit:

℞
Powder of Jalap 12 grains.
Rosin of Jalap 6 grains.
Vitriolated Tartar, half a scruple.
Mercurius Dulcis, half a scruple.
Amber Powder, 6 grains.

Oil of Cloves, 3 drops.
Crabs Eyes Powdered, 6 grains.
Conserve of Rosemary Flowers, 1 dram.

The which I made into a Bolus or Ball and then approaching the beggar did suddenly thrust it down his throat and tickled the back of his palate with the handle of a Horn Spoon so that willy-nilly he had to swallow it at one Gulp; this to prevent him holding it in his mouth and later spewing it forth, as is sometimes the custom of these ignorant folk. Then to bleed him thirty ounces with one of my ivory lancets and so to leave him, hoping that by these measures his Distemper may abate. (Mem: Dr. Leeds says: that Cathartícks should never be given but with a design to Empty some Superabounding Humours to wit, Serous, Phlegmatic, Cholerick, Saline, or Acid. Here in this case of Lues Venerea the blood is stocked with Acrimonious Salts, these irritating the Brain and oppressing the Ducts of the Skin, so that the beggar is Hysterick and Nervous; the cathartick by purging cleanses the Liver and unloads this Grievous Cargo through its channels.)

Assisted at another Parturition, this being a tolerably easy one, but Mr. Rickard did afterwards take us to the Autopsy Room to show us the body of a wench brought into the Infirmary late last night very far gone with The Parturient Fever; which he had been preparing for us before the woman was taken with her Pains; the which I thought kindly of him, as such a busy man has little time to prepare Specimens for Students. The Autopsy very instructive; much pussy inflammation about the cervix and into the body of the Uterus, and the Peritoneum about engorged and studded with minute hæmorrhages or Petechiæ. The structure of the organs normal and the bones of the Pelvis not distorted in any way, and Mr. Rickard informs us that this case most likely met her death by too much interference from the Mid-wife; but this was stoutly denied by a nurse passing through the room who avowed that the wench had not been half-an-hour in Delivering and the Mid-wife little to do but bite the cord; on which Mr. Rickard suggests that she was with her first child and the opening of the Tender Organs of Generation caused her to catch a Rheum in her belly; but this also the nurse denies, saying that the wench had been the Mistress of Three Men to her knowledge and had had God knows how many bastards; at which Mr. Rickard smiles and says that it is mighty probable therefore that her Vitality was exhausted and Unable to Throw Off the Placenta; this being a Dead or Moribund thing at Birth and therefore liable to afflict the Tender Womb with an Enervating Distemper.

To walk in the city afterwards with Mr. Blumenfield and to buy myself a mulberry Cloak, very fine, 27/—.

IV

December 19.

At the Infirmary this day did find the Beggar much subdued the Cathartick having worked with fury and stimulated the Peristalsis of His Guts so that they rid his body of much poison, he having had stools since yesterday. The woman we delivered not so well; suckling her child, but complaining of pains in the lower part of her belly; for which Mr. Rickard had bled her and applied blisters over her navel. Under the eye of my teacher did remove a hand from a Sempstress she having run a needle into the base of the second finger some three weeks back and this had festered so that the poison had burst out near the bones of the wrist, and the base of the fingers very black and green and foul, the skin puffy and crackling on pressure. Thanks to my having been diligent with my anatomising and having made a preparation of the wrist was able to perform this operation with comparative ease, to my great satisfaction. The woman being seated and held securely the afflicted arm was stretched out with the hand held in the position of Supination, the thumb abducted, and I cut a long flap from the Palm to the base of the wrist; then Doctor Urquehart turned the hand into the Pronated position and I cut a half-circle across the back of the wrist; dissected away those structures immediately beneath the skin, severing the Tendons of the Extensor Muscles and the ligaments at the wrist, and secured the Vessels with cords; then folded the long Palmar flap across the stump and stitched it in place with Silk Thread trusting that God would in his Mercy grant that all would knit together healthily. Doctor Urquehart did speak kindly to the woman throughout my cutting, but her fortitude breaking down after the first minute he did give her a Sponge on which to bite her screams being somewhat piercing. And so she was carried to her bed and I to rid myself of some of the blood with which I was spattered.

December 21.

To church with the Hunts, the weather still continuing very cold. Was thankful for my new cloak.

December 22.

Today at the Infirmary did learn that the woman delivered on the 18th. was convulsed yesterday, and found her today moribund and her extremities cold, and she died within an hour, her babe being suckled by another woman delivered last week.

December 23.

Busy today with my anatomising, the trunk nearly finished. With Mr. Rickard's assistance delivered a woman with much sweat and labour and trust that God will be merciful to her and grant that my efforts do not go for naught. The beggar growing violent and despite rigorous treatment more curious in his fancies, so that he will likely be sent to Bedlam. The progress of his foot continues good, the which to my mind is proof of the Gulf between the Vital and Animal Spirits; his Vital being sadly clouded, but his Animal remaining unimpaired so that his wound does sturdily mend itself. Am reminded thereby that I forgot to record that last Saturday I again visited the curious Mr. Kelly at Golden Square and found many gentlemen there with whom pleasant discourse concerning the Origin of Life and the Human Soul, interrupted at the half after nine by the Shrew who arrived vilely foxed swearing like a Covent Garden carter; at which the meeting broke up, but not before the presumptuous doxy had seized the wig of one Mr. Turnbull a Chymist and thrown it into the fire; whereby he had to go home with his head bound in his kerchief. The Clerk removed this day at his request to his lodgings; he is rash to move so early his Wound still being tender, but he desires to spend Christmas at his own home.

December 24.

My dissection of the trunk now finished and to wonder where the next subject is to come from; can see that we shall perforce have to Raid that Miserable Graveyard again, unless the Doctor can obtain a copse from the Authorities. It is Intolerable that the progress of our Art should depend upon such uncertain foundations. Have heard that one Professor Rondelet of Montpelier University did for want of subjects dissect the body of his own child before his class; the which I can well believe. At the Infirmary did find my Sempstress doing well possessed of only a slight fever the which I did remedy with a Diaphoretick, to wit:

℞
Salt of Wormwood and Volatile Salt
and Armoniack, of each three grains.
Ginger Powder 12 grains.
Sugar Candy, 10 grains.
Oil of Cloves, one drop.

This to relieve the body by putting the Blood in Motion and force the pores of the skin gummy with the Humours so that by a gentle sweat they are passed from the body.

(Mem. a Diaphoretick not possible in a poor Institution but spoken highly of by the Authorities contains:

℞
Diaphoretick Antimony, 1 scruple.
Troches of Vipers, half a dram.
Prepared Pearl, half a scruple.

Syrup of Coral, One ounce and a Half.
Bezoartick Vinegar and Treacle Water of each One Ounce.
Oil of Sulphur, a sufficient quantity.
Tincture of Roses, half an ounce.
Make into a draught to be taken at one drink.

To this the Ancients did of Old Times add Gold Water and the Moss from a dead man's skull; but this being hard to come by powdered Earth Worms may be added should the drink not prove Efficacious at the first ingestion.)

I did also gently move the bowels of my sempstress with Nine grains of Gamboge; and then she being comfortable did give her a shilling to buy for herself and the two women in bed with her some Comfits from the sellers of such things, who at this season do come into the Hospitals and the Wards thereof that the Patients may buy Wine and Sweetmeats. I did also visit the old man Ned's friend and finding him in need of a nightcap did buy him one, and gave him a shilling also to buy himself Merriment.

December 25.

Christmas Day. Was awoke early this morning by singing of Carols very tuneful and the ringing of the Churchbells, and on leaning from the landing window did see the Waits below; eight of them, six men and two women, one of the men having a fiddle, another a flute and a third a small trumpet; and so to dress myself with haste and with Mr. Hunt and his wife and the maid-servant into the street to sing very pleasantly with them

In Bethlehem City this day is born, etc.

and so finishing, indoors again, where we did bid each other Abundance of Happiness and Good Cheer; and so to breakfast. I had bought Mr. Hunt a pen-knife with the handle inlaid with silver and Mrs. Hunt a work-box with a picture of Westminster Abbey painted on the lid, and they were vastly pleased with these little gifts, giving me in return a neckerchief all worked by Mrs. Hunt herself. I did give the serving wench two shillings, and after breakfast opened a box delivered by the carrier yester eve; which my worthy host and spouse had slyly laid aside till this moment, this proving to be from my Aunt and Uncle and containing a letter from each, also a Pair of Enamelled Shoe Buckles and a Pair of Gloves of very fine soft leather, and a raised pie and a current cake and a pound of the Best Apples from their Orchard; at which gift I was mighty pleased. To church with Mr. and Mrs. Hunt, and to hear a Good Sermon on the Birth of Christ and all that it Meant in Deliverance from Sin to the World; very interesting, but Lord it did put me in doleful mind of my Hospital and the poor creatures there with their babies, to say nought of the others all groaning under the Pain of their Diseases, so that I was mightily depressed until I did see how perchance I might lighten their load a little that day.

To dine with my friends Mr. Blumenfield, Mr. Pope and Mr. St. Clair at the Leaping Hart off a roasted goose stuffed, with a pudding to follow stuck full of raisins and plums, with which to drink very good Ale, the Inn being the best I have found in London town for Malt Liquor. After to drink Tea and play cards, and I to suggest the idea come to me that morning in Church; at which they were vastly diverted. So with them into the streets these very crowded the day being fine, and to walk until we did find what we sought, to wit a Troupe of Strolling Actors with a Punch and Judy Show, also some Jugglers; with whom we did make agreement that they should hire themselves to us, and so to lead them into the Hospital, the Nurses according to their natures smiling or grumbling; and so with our Actors from Ward to Ward, and Lord, it was a tonic to see how the poor folk did laugh! Mr. Jamie did arrive all bloody from an Operation and he to join us in distributing sundry delicacies that we had bought, and so the afternoon passed in all merriment. And so we left the Hospital again and dismissed the Actors and to a Supper at an Inn in Fleet Street called The Rainbow Tavern, where we met certain merry fellows two of them friends of Mr. St. Clair. We supped off a Roast and some Game and afterwards did gather in an upper room around a fine fire where we did seat ourselves at wine and sundry wights essayed songs. One tall handsome gentleman in a fine scarlet coat and heavy peruke sang very sweetly a song of Motteux's:

Man is for woman made
  And woman made for man
As the spur is for the jade
  As the scabbard for the blade
  So man's for woman made
  And woman made for man—

To which St. Clair, who had attempted to towsle the serving wench and been scratched for his pains, retorted with a Satire on Marriage,

Like a dog with a bottle tied close to his tail
Like a Tory in a bog, or a thief in Jail—

at which we did all laugh heartily, the more so as Mr. St. Clairs voice is a doleful bellow peculiar apt for such a Dismal Catch. The company did call upon me for a song, and with much reluctance I did rise to my feet and gave them a Country refrain, this to my relief proving to their taste, and so we all to singing the Choruses until the candles were nigh blown out. One gentleman did then jump upon the table and imitate a Female in Distress, with sundry shrieks and howls so realistic that Mr. St. Clair still missing his serving wench did in the confusion of his wits pounce upon him and bear him to the ground where they were with difficulty separated. It was suggested that both should be bled to cool their Ardour, but the gentleman in the scarlet coat would not agree, saying that the only blood to be shed that night was The Blood of The Grape; at which all did cheer lustily, and so to bear Mr. St. Clair and his friend from the room to find an ewer of water with which to souse them. But this being hard to come by the scarlet coated wight knocks at a door and receiving no answer opens it; at which Terrific Shrieks from within, there being a wench there in her shift. The handsome gentleman makes a leg and asks her pardon and the landlord arrives and we not liking the tone of his converse to bear him down to the street and put him into his own horse-trough; and then missing Mr. Pope upstairs again and find him trying to get into the wench's bed, she squalling and crying on all the saints to deliver her; and a short man bursts out of a door adjoining and nearly knocks down Mr. Blumenfield on which we not liking *his* converse did carry *him* downstairs he being in his nightshirt and put him in the horse-trough; and so that he might not catch a distemper to carry him upstairs again and put him to bed with the wench (removing Mr. Pope by vis-a-Tergo), and locking the door on them both in all decency.

And so back to our room, where we find Mr. St.

Clair's friend singing very doleful to himself in front of the fire, but no signs of Mr. St. Clair. So to singing again until the dawn appears, and I to go home, and entering the street take a wrong turning into an Alley where I find Mr. St. Clair leaving a house the serving wench at the door all Untidy. So home with him in all comfort and friendliness.

This morning of the 26th. do find my head aches and my stomach recoils from Vittles; shall rest in my lodgings.

December 27.

This day at the Infirmary did find my sempstress doing well the wound suppurating healthily and to my joy the Ligatures about the Vessels have sloughed out without Hæmorrhage; for which may God be thanked. Her fever within bounds; did bleed her a little and after gave her a Febrifuge Pill to wit:

℞
Powdered Peruvian Bark half an ounce.
Oil of cinnamon, two drops.
Powdered Red coral, quantity sufficient as excipient;

of this I did make eight pills and give them to the nurse one to be given each night and morning in a little Barley Water.

The woman I delivered also doing well, as also her child. Did with Doctor Urquehart and George Blumenfield reduce a Hernia on a coachman by the aid of Two Seton Needles, also lanced a Psoas Abscess (this by myself) and reduced a dislocation of a Milkwoman's Arm, she having slipped the Head of the Humerus from its socket in picking up a pail. This is a tedious business performed round the bedpost with many ropes, the dislocation proving stubborn; but to reduce it at last. Then Doctor Urquehart did desire to see the state of the stump of the Sempstress; so to unbandage it again, and he well satisfied with my skill, and so away to a fashionable appointment, whilst I and his other young gentlemen with Mr. Rickard to the Lying-in Ward. There at his bequest George Blumenfield and I did deliver a Woman of a fine son and much fatigued ourselves at it; then to turn and find him and the other gentlemen all pressing round a second case where the Child was presented the Breech First; and he using the forceps but even so unable to deliver her. I and my three friends to help him but the other gentlemen growing weary after two hours did go away and we stayed until eight of the clock that night, when Mr. Jamie having joined us the child was at last got away; only then to find that there was a second within, dead. So to administer stimulants to the poor quean—prepared by Mr. Rickard and contained Savin Juice, White Wine, Borax, and White Sugar—and to burn Shavings of Hartshorn under her nose—and so by infinite trial to remove the second Embryo; and I did think to see her die forthwith from Sheer Languor of Spirits, only we rallied her with Powdered Peruvian Bark and Camphor. Then I to the pharmacy and prepared a Dressing or Solution, namely:

℞
Borax and Troches of Myrrh, half a dram of each.
Cinnamon, one scruple.
Barley Cinnamon Water, two ounces.

With which at Mr. Rickard's directions I did paint the Vulva.

Then Mr. Jamie to insert a Pessary compounded of Myrrh Powdered One Dram, Black Ellebor and Staves-acre of each One Dram, Oil of Amber to make the mass; and this he rolls in Wool and thrusts within the Pudendum; and Lord Lord it was after ten o'clock when all was done, and then our labours not finished. For the wench I had delivered very feverish and restless, and so to bleed her and give a Potion containing Powdered Poppy Seeds in Cinnamon Water. I do wonder whether those ministering in such places do ever get any rest; as we left a fat nurse comes running, bawling that the beggar is taken of a Frenzy and like to murder them all; at which Mr. Jamie swears most furious and sets off at a run with Mr. Rickard at his heels and we to follow him; and into the men's wards where we find the beggar out of bed and strangling the old man Ned's friend, shouting that he was a Devil but that he should not drag him down to Hell; and all the other patients screaming too such a Hubbub as my pen cannot describe. Mr. Jamie seizes the beggar and pulls him back and the beggar turns on him and throws him across the bed; and Mr. Rickard and I pounce on the beggar and endeavour to loosen his grasp, the which we cannot do he having the Strength of Ten Men in his madness; and so we struggle over the poor old man in bed till Grge. Blumenfield snatches up a pot and breaks it over the beggars head. Then we do discover that the dressing is off his foot and there is blood everywhere; so I tear off a strip off the bed-clothes and clap on a Tourniquet and so we carry him back to his bed, where the Assistants bind him with ropes and Mr. Jamie, having taken a stoup of wine, sets to work to shave his head and then claps on a blister containing Spanish Flies one dram, Leaven half an ounce, Honey two drams, to distract the beggars wits from the Fury at his brain to the skull; then throws up a Mercury Clyster and then the beggar having recovered claps more of the blister on his chest and belly; and so we leave him, and I and Mr. Blumenfield to our lodgings, I for one more tired than I have been since I helped our village horse-leech drag the Squire's Horse from the river, some three years back.

December 28.

At church this morning, and in the afternoon to the Infirmary, where I found the beggar dead, he having struggled all night so that they were unable to control the Hæmorrhage from his foot; and the woman that I delivered and the one that had Twins both very sick and feverish, vomiting and complaining of pains in the belly, with a dry skin and quick hard Pulse. Mr. Rickard had bled and purged them and clapped a blister on their bellies.

December 29.

This morning dissected the heart preserved from my previous Anatomising and then to Infirmary Hall where I found both women delivered on Saturday far gone, their eyes sunk, their bodies feeble and the Pulse very soft; not complaining of Pain in the belly any more; as George Blumenfield and I and the other gentlemen were proceeding with Doctor Urquehart to the Operation Room I catched sight of a Nurse calling Mr. Rickard very soft, and so to nudge Mr. Blumenfield and with him to follow Mr. Rickard to the woman's ward, where after an hour the woman he and I delivered died. Her body was removed and we did Anatomise it, and found all those Signs of the Puerperal Fever that the Ancients speak of. And so with Low Spirits back to the Ward where we found the Priest and a Nun administering the Last Sacrament to Mr. Rickard's case, she being a Catholic. And so he and I went out into the streets and to walk beneath the trees in Saint James Park pondering on the Cause of this Malignant Fever that does so Fiercely gripe women just delivered, and can only assume that it results from the State of Flux into which a Females Body is thrown at her effort to rid herself of Child. I cannot bring myself to believe, as is held by the Clergy, that it is a Natural Punishment laid upon Woman by God for tempting Adam in the Garden; am glad to find that Mr. Blumenfield, who though from Youth is somewhat of a Spark, yet at heart is God-fearing enough, does agree with me.

January 2.

A woman brought in haste into the Infirmary this morning dragged out of Rosamunds Pond—a pool near St. James Park much used for assignations—in which she had drowned herself. Mr. Jamie did try all methods of Restoration but without avail. So her relatives did take her body away. I and my three friends did after dining at the Leaping Hart take a stroll in the Park and to wend our way towards this Pool; only we were distracted by the sight of a Funeral and so with common assent to follow it to the Churchyard, which lay down by the river. To avoid the notice of the mob we did divide our forces, Mr. Pope and I to walk separate.

January 5.

Was up again all last night Corpse Taking. Would have performed the task on the evening of Jan. 3, only Mr. St. Clair had that night to dine with his father, and the new graveyard being a good mile from Doctor Urquehart's we did need all our company. As before the Doctor did lend us his Man, but would know nothing of our doings; and after some discussion we did deem it wise to recruit our numbers, as the streets we were to traverse are roamed at night by Foot-pads, and Bully Boys, the Mohawks and the like. So at the Infirmary that day we did gather the Class together and disclosed to them our plans; at which they did all want to come, but we made them draw lots thus selecting four, and by God's grace did get the most lusty of the crew. And so to gather at the Doctors, and at the half after midnight out into the roads and down to the river; catching glimpse of two lots of Gentlemen of the Road but they not molesting us from the quantity of our numbers. Doctor Urquehart's Servant did take our bringing extra members but ill, asking us why we did not bring also some chairmen with torches and a fife and drum; but to calm him with a guinea and he grumbling to lead the way. The night very dark and bitter cold and the streets thereby empty for which we were duly grateful. The graveyard surrounded by a Very High Wall entered by an Iron Gate, which was locked; at which we were all dismayed, but the Huge Serving Man did produce a Master Key and so we gained entrance.

The graveyard a large one, but we had marked the site of the grave and so found our way to it with tolerable ease, one of the young gentlemen however catching his knee against a Tomb Stone and severely bruising his Patella or Knee Pan; at which he did swear lustily. Then to dig, and by our numbers soon to uncover the coffin; and so to burst it open and drag out the body within, this being a man of some forty years very well developed, at which we were well pleased. Then to drag off his Shroud and the moon comes out faint from behind a cloud and shines on us; at which one young gentleman near took Hystericks, the more so as the Doctor's man drops his spade with a great clatter and cries out with a Fearful Oath that it was his cousin; who had it seems been a Highway Man and but lately caught and hanged; Doctor Urquehart's Servant knowing nothing of this. So we to stuff the body in the Sack, he muttering away beneath his breath; and so with some relief of Spirits out into the Lane again. There we did have the Ill Fortune to find some Mohawks awaiting us, they passing and hearing the noise made when the Body was Stripped. They did set upon us with loud cries and I being one of the foremost was straightaway beaten down into the Gutter, where George Blumenfield did in a minute join me; and I very wroth and thankful that we were in force that we might teach these Bullies and Virgin-Breakers a Lesson. So the fight was joined and I to my feet did tug out my Small Sword and to my great satisfaction did receive the rush of one upon its point so that his arm was pierced the which was a lesson to me of how soft the flesh be during life, when not stiffened by that Coagulation of the Humours called the Rigor Mortis. There were I suppose some half-dozen of them and the fight did wage right heartily until Doctor Urquehart's man forced his way into the press and taking two of the young bucks by the throat did knock their heads together with such force that they were stunned, and so the rest to their heels and we in triumph with the corpse to Doctor Urquehart's, where as heretofore I did pass the night on a couch. This day at the Hospital found my Sempstress doing well, and near rid of her fever; for which may God be thanked.

January 10.

Have these days been busy at my anatomising, the Body being a good one the muscles rounded but free from fat, I having taken a leg to dissect. The Infirmary not so busy the cold weather continuing and suppressing the Noxious Influence of the Atmosphere. A fresh case of Stone in the Bladder admitted this day; did see Doctor Urquehart remove it with The Tongs after some trouble in finding it.

January 11

At church, and to take Tea with the Ramsdens, friends of the Hunts, afterwards.

January 13.

My anatomising progressing; I do grow in knowledge daily and have a tolerable acquaintance now with the Mysteries of the Human Body. Did to Mr. Kelly's last night, but he not lecturing; shall to his house tomorrow night, with Mr. Blumenfield.

January 14.

Have but now returned from Golden Square, where Grge. Blumenfield and I did find the usual company gathered, and a talk in swing concerning Morgagni's Discoveries in Anatomy by the Aid of Lenses; at the which I rejoiced that Mr. Blumenfield might hear something of Value and Interest. Did chiefly learn that the body is a Tortuous Jungle of Tiny Fibres or Tubules, especially in the Kidney; the which I had already guessed, or, not to seem presumptuous, as was supposed by the Ancients; the Gross Fibres in for instance a Muscle being Visible to the Eye; whilst without knowledge of tubules it was supposed that the Kidney filtered the Urine the watery Element of the blood. Am infernal tired; all this talk I find do weary me; shall to my bed.

January 15.

Did see today a very pretty example of the Dexterity of Doctor Urquehart in Operating. I and my three friends and the other young gentlemen of his class were with him in the Operating Theatre watching him and Mr. Jamie pass The Bougie on the man with stone, whom they suspect of concealing others within his bladder; when a man was brought in in haste having a few minutes since fallen from the Bedroom Window of a house adjacent. The reason for his fall was Drink, and between that and his Tumble his wits were all abroad; so he was stretched upon the table and his clothes snatched from him, when we saw that the bone of his left thigh was broken but not protruding, but the Patella below it all crushed and the Shin beneath it, so that his leg stuck out from the other like the arm of the letter Y. The right leg whole but for sundry abrasions, as were his other limbs. The Doctor did take one look at the joint all crushed and bloody with the bones sticking out and then cries for the Amputation Instruments; and these being brought he places his left hand on the man's thigh above where the bone was broken; takes up a sharp-pointed knife and drives it through the thigh below the bone; sweeps it outward to the floor; frees the knife and with it transfixes the flesh of the thigh above the bone; then Mr. St. Clair pulling back these two masses he takes a saw from Mr. Jamie and severs the bone, the leg dropping to the floor; then to tie up the great Artery of the Thigh and the other vessels, and to bring across the flaps and trimming them sews them into place making a Purse shaped wound. All this is under three minutes by Mr. Blumenfield's watch, he taking it out at the moment the man's injury was laid bare, and I greatly to marvel; hardly more blood than would fill a small bucket being shed, and it over quickly enough no more than to sober the man.

Doctor Urquehart did then turn to the Man with Stone, who had leapt from the table when the Amputating commenced and was now shivering in a corner hiding himself beneath his blanket, and to resume his search for the Stone; but the fellow being seized with a Shivering and an Acute Vomiting he did send him back to his bed, and to discourse to us of that State of the Faculties which results from Injury to the Head or Wits, as in this recent fall from a Window. He told us that there was much confusion between two states; one was merely the effect of Shock, but the other more serious, indicating Injury to the Substance of the Brain and its coats, from a broken bone of the Skull and the like. In the latter we have he tells us A Diminished Sensibility, a Torpor, with the Pupil of the Eye dilated; the patient may be shaken but you will never rouse him, nay, you may Bawl in his ear or Sound a trumpet in it without arousing Interest. In the former however we have a Transient State; the Wits are shaken, but when the man is put into a warm bed so that his circulation is set in motion he becomes no more insensible than in a very deep sleep; you may rouse him if you call his name, the Pupil of his Eye is not Dilated, nay it may even be Contracted; and to illustrate this to us the Doctor takes us to the man's bed, he lying in a Swoon very pale, and his brows puckered; but on one of the friends who had brought him in shouting his name in his Ear very loud he did stir and mutter faintly; so the Doctor to show us that this was therefore a Stunning or Temporary Suppression of the Faculties. In all these cases one may bleed; nay it is imperative that one does do so that the Brain may be relieved; but Doctor Urquehart did say that there would be enough Hæmorrhage from his leg for this purpose, and so to cover him warmly and leave him to Gather himself together.

January 16.

Vastly pleased with my Skull of the Hanged Woman now a fine specimen very clean which I have brought home with me and set on the tallboy; to the scaring of the serving wench, who cannot be persuaded that it will not harm her. At the Infirmary did find the Man Tumbled from the Window quite recovered, though still weak; and so to Mr. Rickard and more Parturitions, and three more

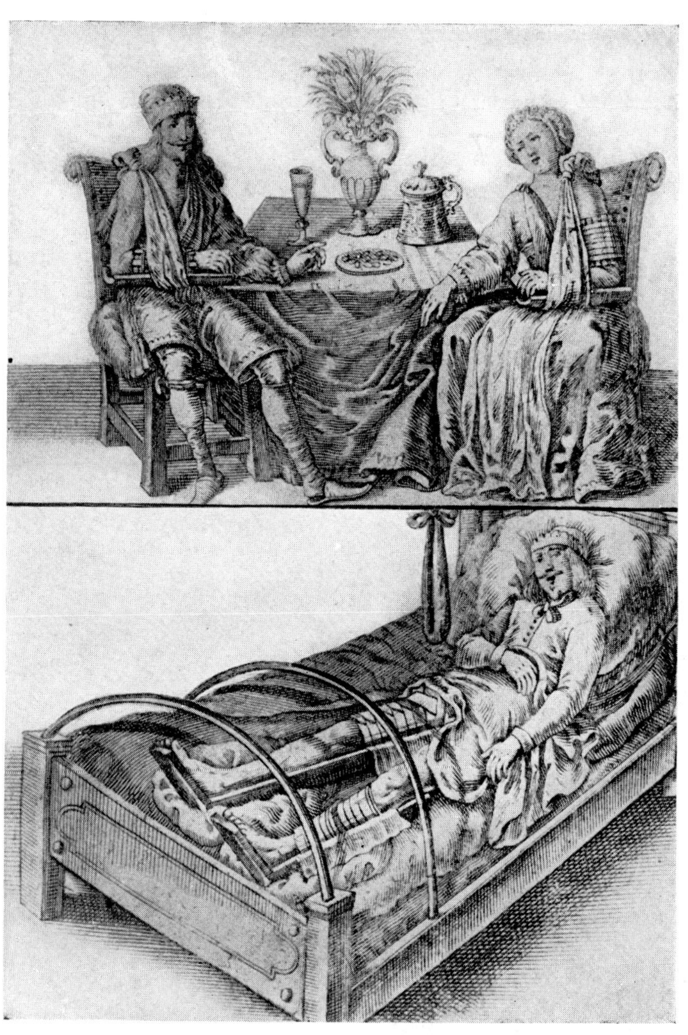

Bandaging Methods in the Eighteenth Century

(FROM WIEDEMANN)

children, two girls and a boy, born. Have been instructed to say nothing of the previous cases of the Puerperal Fever lest the women grow Hysterical.

January 18.

To church, and a very long sermon on the Ascent.

January 21.

A very pleasant evening last night. To the Theatre with my Three Friends, where we did see Mrs. Stanley in the Tyranny of Love, this a pretty conceit very light and enjoyable, Mrs. Stanley a most catching wench. The play a Study of Love through the Ages; so that we had Samson and Delilah, with some dancing beauties most diverting; and Good King Hal and his wives; and the Turkish Court with more of the dancing girls, very saucy and but scantily clad despite the time of year; at which I was pleasantly stirred, and if this be truth—as I am assured it is—could almost wish myself A Grand Vizier. A good orchestra there and some fine singing by Mrs. Stanley. The play lasted some two and a half hours with a Pause of some fifteen minutes when the Orange Girls did hand round fruit and sweetmeats; these girls being naught but Whores and ogling the Bucks and one saucy quean even inviting yr. ob. servant; at which I was mightily perturbed and like to have Gone with her, only by the grace of God she stooping I did see her dugs and one of these Foul with a Sore; so that I would have no more of her; and so after leaving the Theatre to a tavern with my three friends, there to sup lightly and take a night-cap of mulled wine.

January 23.

Mr. St. Clair and Mr. Pope, who have been dissecting the head of the Resurrected Man, vastly diverted this morning to find a Fracture of the Base of His Skull; this having caused an Extravasation of those vessels in that Region, and we to discuss whether this Injury was inflicted before or after Death; Doctor Urquehart to settle the point by pointing to the Amount of Blood Shed, which indicates that Death succeeded the Injury; this inflicted we know not how, but suppose that it was in His Capture. At the Infirmary did find the Man with Stone tolerably comfortable, Mr. Jamie having found a small quantity of Gravel in his Bladder which he had washed out with a Squirt. I at his direction to the Pharmacy there to prepare a Diuretick, namely:

℞
The Inner Rind of the Elder one pugii.
Roman Wormwood half a handful.
Gentian Root half a dram.

Infused in Warm water; to be given at pleasure in Barley Water.

Gave Humble Thanks to God to find my sempstress doing well, the wound quite healed, all the stitches sloughed out. It is remarkable how one so ill-nourished can yet rally to heal a wound in the Body's Continuity. Mr. Rickard did give us an intriguing lecture on those diseases of Women that appear after Parturition, especially that Hysterick or Passion which takes them some hours or some days after the Child has been delivered; the which is a kind of Gladness of the Body to be rid of its load.

V

January 24.

My dissecting of the leg progresses. Am diverted by the multitude and intricate disposal of the Nerves; Doctor Urquehart does inform me that each Nerve is a bundle of tiny tubes wrapped for protection in a Membrane analagous to the Dura Mater of the Brain; these tubes serving as Canals or Channels for the Animal Spirits, which flow from the Brain as the body has need of them.

January 25.

Sunday, and to church. A day of rest to reflect upon all the wonders that I have seen.

January 28.

Much excitement this morning as I pass to the Infirmary with my friends. Great shouting in the streets and the firing off of pistols and blunderbusses, and then the Street emptied like magic at a cry of Mad Dog, and we to jump hastily into a door as a black cur comes chasing down the road his jaws all frothy snapping and biting at whatever lay in his path. A tall soldier with one eye steps out into the road and as the dog makes for him clubs it over the head with his stick; at which shouts of acclamation from the surrounding houses, and my friends to aid a fat man over whom the dog had jumped, he throwing himself into the gutter to avoid it, and I to peer curious at the carcase of the dog. This no more than a pup, and as it lay in the road with its mouth open did see that its gums were all swollen; at which I did suspect that it was no Mad Dog, but one driven Hysterick by the Pain of Deliverance of its teeth; as has been told me by the Horse-Leech at home, and as I have seen children near distracted from the same cause.

To join my friends gathered about the fat man, he blubbering and calling on God to aid him, he determined that the Cur's Teeth had met in his flesh, though no signs of this. But we did on searching find a Spot on his Buttock on the Left Side where the cloth was torn; and at this the soldier did run down the Street and fetched a Smith who coming in haste with a hot coal held in his tongs, did clap this to the fat man's seat; and so he leaps to his feet screaming as though the Dog had bitten him in very truth; and so he turning violent the soldier and the smith did lay hands on him and hustled him into the gates of our Infirmary; where Mr. Jamie, hearing first their tale, and then ours, did with a faint smile deliver him to the Attendants, who tearing his clothes from him, did then hurry him into a Large Tub filled with cold water, in which they did submerse him holding his head beneath water until he was near choked; and then to hustle him all dripping out of the water and to flog him with towels; and so he was put to bed and Mr. Jamie did bleed him some six ounces; and we much edified to Mr. Rickard for instruction in the Midwifery.

January 29.

At the Infirmary this day did find the fat man of yesterday gone home, he not thankful for our efforts to relieve him of Fear of becoming Mad, but saying that Mad Dog or No he would rather die in his own bed, than be hounded into An Early Grave. The sempstress sister to see her, and to inform her that she might have the woman home with her before the week was out.

February 1.

A sermon today on the Parable of the Sower; the day being fine to walk in the fields after.

February 3.

Two cases of the Spotted Fever admitted this day to the Infirmary.

February 4.

With Mr. Kelly and my four friends to the Museum of the Royal Society in Crane Court, a narrow court leading off Fleet Street. Vastly interesting. Amongst the exhibits were some most rare and curious brought from the Farthest Corners of the Globe, that I doubt not do not exist elsewhere in England. Quoting from a catalogue for which I paid Two Shillings—this not dear, for the pamphlet does contain much rare information—I note these that did catch my Imagination and Amuse and Instruct my Mind:

A Bone from a Mermaid's Head. (This curious like the bone of my Hanged Woman's Head.)

The Leg Bone of an Elephant, till recent supposed the leg of a Giant.

A Tortoise; his grease good for the scurvy; said when turned on his back to Sigh and Fetch Abundance of Tears.

A White Shark, said to swallow men whole; and the Harpoon with which such beasts are catched.

A Humming Bird and his Nest; a lovely beast, said to weigh but twelve grains, but more Gorgeous in his Dress than the Sultan I did see at the Theatre.

The Quill of a Porcupine, which when enraged the creature can shoot at his enemy.

A Large Whale, and a picture of one rending a Boat.

The Flying Squirrel, which, the Pamphlet informs me, can ford a River on the Bark of a Tree, erecting his Tail for a Sail.

Some Petrifactions of Divers Shapes, all very curious.

And many other Rare and Astonishing Things and creatures, all of which did fan a Flame first set smouldering in me by the tales of the sailor Ned, to one day Sail the Oceans and see all these strange things for themselves; they being beautiful now, but how much more so amongst their Natural Homes!

Mr. Kelly did also take us into an upper room furnished with a long table down the centre and benches round the walls where the Society does hold its meetings. We did see the Silver Gilt Mace very fine, placed before the President when the Society is Sitting.

February 5.

The Sempstress home today, but to warn her that she must treat the Stump of Her Wrist with much care, it still being tender and likely to bleed on a blow. The cases of the Spotted Fever but ill; one fellow in what is I fear a decline, the other Raging in a Hectic Fever. So to bleed them both, and to throw up the Bark; this being good both to abate the Fever and as an Alterative. The man with gravel sleepy but his pulse good; he should make a good recovery; he is Wetting without discomfort; not so the man tumbled from the Window; he has a Low and Persistent Fever. To bleed him also.

February 6.

Have this day finished my anatomising of the leg, and Doctor Urquehart to inform us that he had bespoke us a New Body that of a Man to be hanged on Monday; he to be tried today having been taken slitting a purse last Saturday, and thereby his conviction a certainty; Doctor Urquehart knowing the Judge and bespeaking his corpse before any other Hospital knoweth of it.

February 9.

This day to another Hanging, thereby as George Blumenfield did put it to see that Our Future Subject was Killed Properly in all Christian Charity. The weather cold, but the day fine with something of a wind; so that a tolerable large crowd was gathered, and a number of the gentry; there being two other men to be Hanged besides Ours, also an old old Woman suspected of poisoning her grandson; and she being so very old and destitute the Judges had sentenced her so that she might have an easy Passing. The other two men a Contrast; one a poor wight a Grocer who had given wrong change to a customer and after drawn a knife on him in Wrath; the other a fine sturdy Rogue a Highway Man who had kept the Town in suspense these three months past; robbing the Mails twice, and Lord knows how many private coaches, shooting one coachman dead; and making a Fight for it when taken, so that he came to the Gallows with his head bound up and his arm all bloody; but not thereby disturbed, but dressed in a fine bottle-green coat and knee-boots; waving to the crowd and strutting to the last, so that the Mob did cheer him, hissing the poor Grocer who was in the same cart with him but never ceased to Moan and Cry Aloud. These two and Our Man all turned off at once, the Highway Man taking the rope from the Hangman and bowing adjusting it about his own neck; at which a Fine Lady in a coach nearby cries out despairingly; and he to make her a leg and throw her a Kiss; she being I learn later one of the Ladies whom he had held up; she later relenting, and giving him Great Joy, to wit becoming His Mistress. And so they were turned off; and after some ten minutes the Hangman cuts Our Man and the Grocer down, but leaves the Highway Man swinging; and then Ropes the Old Beldame, she, I do verily believe, having no sense of what they were about to do to her, but chuckling and crowing in the manner of the Very Aged; and so the Hangman cries "Heigh Mother Witch, Up to the Skies With You!" at which the crowd laughs, and then she joins the Highway Man; and the Hangman leaves her to twitch and sway in the wind whilst his Assistant stokes the fire beneath a Cauldron of Tar and they prepare their Instruments.

Then the Assistant cuts down the Highway Man

and they lay him on the floor and take off his clothes; at which more screeches from the Lady aforesaid and a gentleman with her to Apply Smelling Salts; and the Hangman shaves the Highway Man's Head and then he and the Assistant Disembowel him, and shove him into the Cauldron of tar; then they Fix the Irons round him, and so to swing him once more to the Gibbet, where they leave him to dry in the wind as a Warning to all such Malefactors. The old woman now cut down and she and the Grocer driven off in a cart to Surgeon's Hall; and Our Man put into a cart likewise and driven off by the Doctor's huge serving man to Doctor Urquehart's house; and the Hangman and his Assistant to throw the Dice for the Highway Man's clothes; and the Lady aforesaid comes up all of a Sweat and a Fluster and gives them a guinea for a lock of the Highway Man's hair. But Lord women are strange creatures; this being done and she having made I suppose a Decent Show I did see her and the Gentleman with her drive off in the coach he kissing her neck and she clutching his shoulder with such Passion that you would think she had never loved else but him. And so to dine, and later to inspect our body at the Doctor's; it proving to be one of fairish proportions.

February 10.

To dissect the corpse this morning, taking an arm with George Blumenfield; he quoting some doggerel peculiar apt, that he heard at a Tavern last night:

Behold the Villain's dire disgrace
Not Death itself can end
He finds no peaceful resting place
His Breathless Corse no friend.

Torn from the root, that wicked Tongue
Which daily Swore and Cursed!
Those eyeballs, from their Sockets wrung
That glowed with Lawless Lust!

His heart exposed to prying eyes
To pity has no claim
But Dreadful from his Bones shall rise
His Monument of Shame!

The last line of the second verse seeming to me especial apt as applied to the Highway Man, with which sentiment my friends did all agree. Having learnt the infernal Doggerel it has hummed and jingled through my brain throughout today; did find myself bleeding a wight come in with a Surfeit to its metre, the which did exasperate me. One of the spotted fever cases dead; the other violent with his fever which has distracted his Wits so that he grows frantic; Mr. Jamie has bled him one hundred ounces but without avail.

February 11.

Did see a dismal thing at the Infirmary this day, namely the body of my Sempstress, she having drowned herself, the loss of her right hand having deprived her of her means of livelihood; seeing her body I did feel most down-cast as though I were in some way responsible; but God is my witness that I did remove the hand with all the best of intentions and at the instruction of my teacher; could I a surgeon have left her to perish miserably from the Gangrene at her wrist? George Blumenfield and my other two friends to anatomise her, and I to assist them, but I had no heart in it, and so to the Pharmacy to assist Doctor Leeds.

February 12.

Slept but ill last night, disturbed by the Memory of my Sempstress, also the Mother and Child that Mr. Blumenfield and I did Deliver they later dying. Am most distracted in my Wits about the whole matter of Disease and its Moral Bearings. It is easy for the Parsons to preach of original sin, that do not come into the wards of a Hospital; but to my mind it is nonsensical to think that God who we are taught is the God of Love, should for some ancient crime committed by a doxy doom all the rest of her kin. I have seen many in the Wards, poor folk but none the less godly and upright, suffering the tortures of the damned for no good reason that I could see, save that their bodies are corrupt; the which is a Healthy Design of Nature to preserve the Earth from overcrowding and a feature of all of us. Would to Parson Hardy, he a worthy man enough, but his Intelligence limited. Did anatomise this morning and Delivered a Woman this afternoon; do trust that all will go well.

February 13.

By God's mercy the women delivered yesterday do continue in health and their children with them. The Spotted Fever Case doing not so bad; to throw up the Bark, and to assist Mr. Jamie bleed a case of Phthisica Pneumonica or Consumption, he being but low in health and coughing, the Pain very great on the left side where the Body one Supposes is making a Grand Effort to rid itself of the Humours. To bleed him and to cover him warmly with blankets a hot bottle to his feet and stomach; Mr. Rickard is to try to get him Asses Milk, or this failing Boiled Snails; though where either of these are to be found at this season I know not. Did walk in the city with my friends in the afternoon, and to examine sundry books at the Booksellers in St. Paul's Churchyard. In Fleet Street, at Number Thirty Two South Side, at the book-shop of one William Sandby, I did see Doctor Johnson all wrapped in a great cloak turning over the leaves of a tome; and after to see that which had interested him, this being a little Translation of the Odes of Livy written by one Ajax; who this Ajax may be I cannot guess, the only one I have heard of being dead these many years. Did also see at the same shop a copy of that book of which Mr. Kelly has spoken, namely, Baker, on "The Microscope Made Easy," in which I browsed, being greatly diverted by sundry wood-cuts of Itch-Mites and the like; and from this to examine some Volumes of a Great Work on Insects by one Swammerdam, and an Essay by Lesser entitled Insect Theology, this containing some contributions by a Frenchman Lyonet; also a quaint book on a Polyp found in Fresh Waters by Trembley; all of these worthies prosecuting their Researches by the Aid of the Microscope; so that I did see the force of Mr. Kelly's remark that this Machine is the only true Teacher, Worlds Undreamt of being revealed by its Magic; it is in sober fact as the Poet has written

Each Myrtle Seed includes a thousand Groves
Where future Bards may warble forth their Loves.

I was taken from these Wonders by Mr. Pope and turning did find that my other friends were already gone ahead, being Attracted by the gathering of a crowd; and to join them, to find a Watchmaker who had set up a Booth near Durham Yard in the Strand. There on trestles he had set out a tiny Chaise with four wheels, this being mighty small; and then he coaxes a Flea out of a box and sets him to draw it; other fleas being taken out which did turn water mills and march in troupes like soldiers; at which

I was amazed, having never attributed aught of Intelligence to Fleas but a Malignant Instinct. This London be a marvellous place, where one may see more Wonders in ten yards than one would see in ten Miles at home; the which is no doubt why the inhabitants are more hare-brained, constant Surprises shaking the Wits and enervating the Reason.

February 14.

The Consumptive coughing a great deal; the which Mr. Rickard takes as affording proof that our efforts are Sweating the Distemper out of him. To ease his cough did prepare him a Pectoral Julep namely:

℞
Alexiterial Milk Water.
Black Cherry Water.
Wormwood Compound Mirabilis.

Of each One Ounce.

Sal Volatile Oleosum, 10 drops.

To be taken at a draught.

And to ease the Congestion in his Lungs did throw up a Clyster, this compounded of Epsom Salts, Caraway Seeds, and Oil of Amber, of each an ounce; this to distract the Humours from the Tubes of the Bronchiæ to his Guts.

February 15.

At church: and the day being fine, to walk with Mr. Hunt in the afternoon upon the city walls; whence a fine view of the City.

February 19.

My dissection almost done. Severed the foot this morning with intention to make a preparation of the Ligaments of the Ancle. At the Infirmary did find the Consumptive eased; Mr. Rickard not able to obtain either the Asses Milk or the Snails, but do think the fellow will do without 'em, he having we hope passed the Point or Crisis of his Complaint. The Spotted Fever also well; the man will live. Hear that the Jail Fever has broken out again at Newgate, seven prisoners and a turnkey very sick and the worthy Judges in the Court in a Sweat lest there be an outbreak like to that of last year. Did cast up my accounts this night; am greatly disturbed to find that my stock of money grows perilous low.

February 20.

This morning did have a Private Case, one of Mr. Hunts friends summoning me to attend his child, a boy of fourteen years, he being afflicted with a Swollen Gum at the base of a front tooth. This swelling I did on examination find to be an Abscess, and so to lance it and then thinking that the root of the tooth was likely destroyed and the Abscess to come again, did jerk out the tooth before he had gathered what I was about to do; thus it was out before he could squall at which his parents were greatly pleased. It is comic how one grows in Reputation by such small matters; had I attended the wife through a difficult labour, then to lose her by no fault of mine own, I should be thought clumsy and no doctor, despite I had applied all that Art suggests; but through a simple tooth-pulling with moderate pain I am thanked as though I had got him through the Small Pox without blemish.

February 21.

Varnished the Ligaments of my preparation of the Ancle this morning; then with my friends to the Infirmary, where we attended a Labour, Mr. Pope distinguishing himself by the use of a Fillet. The Consumptive uproarious and sitting up in bed spinning rhymes, to the discomfort of the other patients; Mr. Jamie does inform me that such Light-Headedness is oft a feature of those smitten with a Consumption.

February 22.

At church.

February 23.

This morning after anatomising at Doctor Urquehearts in haste to the Infirmary, there to see how the

The Transplanting of Teeth in the Eighteenth Century

(AFTER A COLORED ENGRAVING BY ROWLANDSON)

Woman delivered yesterday fared; and to my great comfort found her Easy and without undue Languor, for which I gave thanks to God. This Puerperal Fever is a Queer and Mysterious Complaint; I am almost tempted to Desert my Principles, and think it in the Nature of a Visitation. It cannot alway be a Wroth of Nature at Man's interference especially through the use of instruments, for I have in my studies here seen it occur both after a Gentle Labour and in one attended with Difficulty, where there was much interference with the Woman, and with the Child by means of the Instrument. But I stubbornly refuse to admit that Any Disease is a Visitation from God who is called the God of Love; no, not even the Frenzies and Madness, where there is certainly cause to think that God has removed the Soul, and left only a Husk.

To talk with sundry other women in the Ward awaiting their time, and to cheer them; then an accident arriving, in haste with my friends to see it. This a poor man who had slipped in the mud beneath a coach a wheel passing over his head so that his scalp was torn and the Bone depressed over the Lower Third of the Parietal Region. Doctor Urquehart was sent for, and coming, takes the sponge that Mr. Jamie was washing away the mud and blood with, and clears the site; then presses it very slightly with his finger and then shakes his head; but then sends for the Instrument saying that one must relieve the pressure on the substance of the Brain beneath; but he suspects that this may be torn beyond hope of repair. And so the man's clothes being taken from him he was wrapped warmly in blankets, and being still stunned no ropes were needed to bind him, and Doctor Urquehart takes up the Bit to Trepan him, and cutting away the skin cuts out the broken portion, and sighs with relief to find the Dura Mater not badly ruptured. The wound was dressed, the man bled, and then removed to a bed near the Consumptive so that the Ward is likely to be lively with two crack brains in it.

February 24.

Did find the Accident case of yesterday still insensible his pulse very weak; do doubt whether he will ever recover. Bled him also the Consumptive, that the latter might not feel neglected; also gave both of them a gentle purge namely a Clyster containing eight grains powdered gamboge.

February 25.

At the Infirmary in the morning. In the afternoon did walk through Tottenham Fields, very pleasant, and to sup with my many friends at the Adam and Eve.

February 26.

The body of our Resurrected Man, or its remains, removed this day by Doctor Urquehart's huge servant, he having bought a plot of land for it in an adjacent graveyard. We did not attend its obsequies. The woman I delivered still well, her child excellent, crying lustily. The wight with the Shivered Skull now awake, but very confused in his wits; did bleed him seven ounces, and throw up a Clyster these to divert his blood from his head.

February 28.

Doctor Urquehart obtained a new body for us this day, a Pauper died in the Workhouse and no one claiming him. An old man with an intolerable number of lice in his hair, the which we did remove by scouring his skull with tar, and so to dissect him, I and Mr. Blumenfield taking the head. At the infirmary did see the Doctor perform three Amputations, one a leg taken off at the Thigh of a young and pretty woman, she having an injury to her knee that would not heal; I to assist him, and was allowed by Mr. Jamie to tie the cords about the great Vessels.

The man with the Broken Skull still all abroad restless and twitching his face, and the Consumptive not so well either, though confoundedly Lively in his Mind, preparing an Epitaph for his neighbour's tombstone should the poor man die, this all larded with fine Latin phrases; and which he insists on reading aloud, so that those desiring to rest are Greatly Disturbed.

March 1.

At church, many of the gentry coming from their houses at Marylebone. Did see amongst them the Fine Lady the Highway Man's Mistress, she with a gallant in whose arms it is plain she has found consolation. Was not certain whether it was the same buck that I did see at the Hanging; I fear me though that whether it be or no the wench is naught but a Trollope. To walk afterwards with Mr. Hunt and his wife, and with them in the afternoon to drink tea at Parson Hardy's.

March 3.

At the Infirmary this day did see the Death of the Man with the Cracked Skull, he having become paralysed along his right side last night and this morning sinking into a Stupor, his breathing becoming fainter and fainter until only a Mirror told us that he was Sped. To anatomise him, and found beneath the Membrane of the Brain called the Dura Mater, on the side that Doctor Urquehart had trepanned, a thick creamy layer of Pus; did notch my knife on his arteries, these being verily almost as hard as stone; a feature that George Blumenfield and I have found in the Head of our Pauper. The operation cases all doing well, even the Woman whose thigh was cut through; this a lucky thing, for these cases do often die forthwith from the Inflammation at the Wound striking inwards at the

Bowels; also the Consumptive, whose condition does swing like a weather-cock; he much distressed because some fellow has stole the Obituary on the Man with the Cracked Skull; so that he cannot perform any Obsequies.

March 6.

At the Infirmary today did see a very touching little thing. Was in the wards examining the wound of the Wench who has had her thigh removed, when I heard a great out-cry behind me, and a young fellow comes bursting in, crying and calling "Mary! Mary!" this being the wench's name; and she sits up with a glad little noise, and I to reprove her lest the motion do start a Hæmorrhage; and then the young man comes to the bed-side and falls on his knees beside it, clasping her with his arms as though he could not believe she were Real; and I to reprove him, lest his antics do disturb the dressing. But he catches sight of the stump of her leg, and his mouth drops open aghast; and she catches hold of him plainly fearing that this Blemish may extinguish his love for her. But Lord the fellow looks at it, and then bursts out crying, saying "My dear, my dear, what have they done to you?" and then they both fall weeping on each others shoulders. So I to move him gently so that he could sit on the bed, and then replaced the bed-clothes, and went in search of Mr. Jamie, the matter being beyond me, and I fearing lest all this excitement do kindle a fever in the woman. But Mr. Jamie hears my tale and then smiles and says nothing until he comes with me to the door of the ward; and then peering in we do see the two young creatures clasping each others hands and her eyes all glowing, and then Mr. Jamie turns back and says to me with another small smile that there be no medicine like Love; and so I left the two together for a quarter of an hour, and then returned, to tell the young man that his Sweetheart was but lately Operated on, and that she is still but weak, and that he must now leave her to recruit her faculties in sleep; but that he may come again later.

And so he left, pausing a dozen times to wave his hand to her and blow her kisses; and all the other patients in the wards sitting up, and half of them in tears, and the other half unwonted quiet, according to their several temperaments. I to soothe the wench and tell her that she must rest; at which she nods and smiles very obedient, but tells me that this her lover was prevented from marrying her seven months back by her aunt, (she being an orphan) and sent by her up to London town to some cousins; she injuring her knee on the coach, so that it mortified with the result that I had seen; and that the young man, the son of a Norfolk farmer, had straightaway set off after her, but had not traced her until this day; at which great happiness for them both. And so home to my supper pondering on this

Strange Intoxicating Distemper of Love; which I have heard described as a Disease, it being Insidious in Onset, Progressive in Course, and Invariably Fatal in Termination; but surely one Affection above all others that one would pray to be Inoculated with; and to wonder also whether the Great Lady finds as much happiness in all her Amours as these two simple Folk have discovered in their Love for each other.

March 7.

A clergyman in the wards at the Infirmary this day, there to wed the two young lovers; so that with a Home and a Stout Man awaiting her there is no doubt that the Wench will make a Good and Speedy Recovery. The Consumptive very low; almost in tears, and to compose a Wedding March; but to comfort him, and to ensure that he shall not try to sing it to the other Patients, bled him at the Temple some six ounces.

VI

March 8.

At church this morning. Did pray for the Future Happiness of the two lovers, though I am sure that after all their Trials God will be good to them and give them Much Happiness. Supped with my three friends in the evening, at Mr. Blumenfield's lodgings in Duck Street, off Leicester Square; Mr. Pope did bring his fiddle, so that we had a very pleasant hour of music.

March 10.

Anatomised at Doctor Urquehart's this morning, my dissection of the head proving vastly interesting. The Doctor, seeing Mr. Blumenfield and I sawing the bone to expose the course of the Optic Nerve, did call the class together, and discoursed to us on the Diseases of the Eye, of the Opthalmia and the Cataract, and the treatment for these. The Opthalmia may be treated with Astringents and Cooling Lotions such as Alum Water and Extract of Plantane mixed; but the Cataract is incurable, being a Perishing of the Lens of the Eye when this exposed over long periods to bright lights, as seen in the Aged; so that it casts a Shadow upon the Optic

Nerve, causing blindness. The Doctor did say also that few Structures of the Body were so Badgered about by Quacks; that even the Physicians deserted what Anatomy could teach 'em to spin notions, so that their wits became addled and they poured such filthy messes as Frog Spawn Water into the Eye on the least provocation. He did entreat us that we as young surgeons should seek diligently to find new methods of Treatment remembering that Surgery being based upon Anatomy is a more certain guide to Health than Physic which being based upon Windy Theorising was too often Mere Empiric. Physic he told us was like to a man on a ship who in a Storm did seek by incantation to Alter the Force of the Wind; unlike like the Surgeon, who in Anatomy learnt the Art of Navigation, so that the Ship and all on her were brought safe to Port; at which analogy we did all clap our hands. And thereby Doctor Urquehart did bid us use our wits when called in to one suffering with his Eyes; not forgetting that the Vessels of the Eye being engorged we should use the General Methods to relieve this Congestion; namely the Seton the Blister the Cathartic; Emetics, at any time dangerous, were here obviously forbidden. His talk did remind me of one Quack, Oculist to Queen Anne, of whom I had heard my uncle quote:

Her Majesty sure was in a Surprise
Or else was very short sighted

When a tinker was sworn to look after her eyes
And the mountebank Reed was knighted.

The said Reed being a tinker turned preacher turned oculist; the which is comment sufficient on the modern standing of the Oculist's art.

March 11.

Was late to Doctor Urquehart's this morning, after breakfast composing a long letter to my uncle telling him of my affairs and how Low my stock of money was getting. I trust that this will not be too great a surprise to him, I in my previous letters having mentioned nothing of this side of my life to him. And so to seal it, and to take it to the coach with my own hands, trusting that the Mails will not be robbed and my Labours go for naught. Then to the Doctor's, and after a short while Anatomising with my friends to dine at the Leaping Hart; from there to the Infirmary. Did find the young wife doing well, her husband with her reading to her, and all the Ward listening; flowers round her, so that the place looked like an Arbour. The Consumptive better; all this Romance has diverted his mind, so that he mends apace. At the Pharmacy did help Doctor Leeds fill up the Stock Medicine Jars, the contents of these running low.

March 13.

The Consumptive again much improved, and Mr. Rickard, hearing that he has a distant relative a

Farmer on the Essex coast, to prompt him to go there; country air being no doubt better for one about to die than the Miasmas of an Hospital. The Young Woman somewhat low; the cords about the Great Vessels have sloughed out, and most of the stitches but there is still much Morbid Activity at the wound; put on new dressings, and bled her, and threw up the bark; also, at Mr. Jamie's suggestion, did administer a purge of Epsom Salts and Jalap.

March 15.

At church, and to meet my three friends after, in the afternoon, for a walk; the day being fine and sunny we were tempted to walk to Hampstead, which we did, a very pleasant saunter through the fields and meadows of Tottenham Fields and Kentish Town, passing an old Inn once the haunt of that strange old witch Mother Shipton; thereby to discuss one of her sayings, namely "That horses without carriages should go," we wondering how this might be done; George Blumenfield suggesting Wind, Mr. Pope Steam, on the principle of those Engines already designed by Philosophers. Hampstead a pretty village, set on a hill from whence one has a mighty fine view of the City, it rising from the fields all smoky and misty, a fit subject for a Painter. Did see the Assembly rooms where there were a number of the gentry these having driven out in their coaches to take the Waters. Did sample these, they very clear and pleasant, with a slight irony tang; and so to walk on through a long lane to an opposing village, Highgate, where there is an Inn famous for being the meeting place of the Wits and Philosophers. Our road did take us past the grounds of the new house of my Lord Mansfield, and a little further on Mr. St. Clair points out to us a lane that runs down into the woods to a Duelling Ground; this lane famous for the Nightingales that do lodge in the trees about. And so to Highgate, where we passed a fine Inn set at the top of a hill, and I to think it was the one of which Mr. Blumenfield had spoken, but this a little further on, a smaller place but cleanlier, set in a clearing hedged about by fine trees, and called The Flask. Here also we did find some of the gentry, these taking their wine about a fire that was most welcome, the evening having set in chilly. We did sup there, and then home by coach, hailing it from the Hill, and so back to our lodgings in a pleasant glow, thankful to have made the return journey without harm from the thieves and foot-pads that do infest the lanes at night.

March 16.

On visiting the Infirmary this afternoon was greatly pleased to find the young bride Much Improved and I do not doubt that now she will mend without further Incident. Bled the Consumptive; he is to leave here tomorrow. Assisted the Doctor with a reduction of the dislocated wrist of a coachman who had tumbled off his box; also a lancing of an abscess on the thumb of a carpenter, and thereby to find a splinter in the depths of it. There was a man new come in with a Dropsy, that sagged his belly almost to his knees; he very short of breath, and his heart laboured; for in Dropsy we have the Mechanicks of Anatomy—the fluid that oozes out from the Indolence of the Absorbents runs into the most pendant parts, and fills these like a bucket, rising about the Fork where the Aorta divides into the Iliac Arteries until the blood there is dammed back into the Heart. Mr. Jamie did seat him, with his belly resting upon a support, and then handing the Trocar to me, requests me to Tap him; this by the grace of God I knowing how to do, I plunged it in at a point a little further down than half way between the Navel and the Os Pubis on the imaginary line of the Linea Alba; withdrew the Stilet, and there ran forth enough of fluid to fill a basket, the man being carefully watched by Mr. Jamie that he did not faint, the sudden relief to the Arteries oft causing this. Then to the Pharmacy, there to prepare him medicine to be given him each morning by the nurse; this compounded of Oxymel of Squills and Syrup of Horehound, of each three Ounces, mixed in a Sufficient quantity of Fox-glove Water. Mr. Rickard to inform me that in most cases of Distemper it is a Very Wise Plan to keep the bowels lax, and particularly in these cases where the Body struggles against a Surfeit of Humours; so he will receive with his drink small quantities of Calomel and Jalap mixed.

The Young Wench progresses, her husband with her nigh all the day; the Consumptive I did see go to the country this day, he in no wit disturbed by the knowledge that the Shadow of the Wings is over him; but reading out a farewell speech, and then embracing Mr. Rickard, Mr. Jamie and sundry students in turn, and turning at the door to Strike an Attitude at Doctor Leeds bawling "Ave Cæsar! Morituri te salutant!" the old gladiators' Salute; the which I did think brave of him, and to ponder on the wondrous Compensations that God does afford to them mortally stricken by Sickness.

March 18.

Dissected this morning, the head of the old man finished and George Blumenfield to make a preparation of the bones. Have been to Mr. Kelly this night, and had a squint through his Microscope at the Animalculæ found in the teeth and the urine, wondrous interesting. Would be more intrigued if I thought that these tiny creatures had any say in the Health or Sickness of the body; but it seems that they are Generated De Novo from the Heat and the Salts; although one Spallanzani held that this was not so, but that each bore children, each after its kind; but they are too few in number to Affect the Body as a Whole, though it is of course possible that their antics do in teeth bruise the Tartar and cause the Quick within to ferment the tooth so blackening.

March 19.

With my three friends to St. George's Hospital, there to hear a lecture by one William Hunter on the Generation of Animals, Doctor Urquehart having expressed a wish that we should do so. This man Hunter a example of the Curious Instruments God does choose to forward his Ends; he having been apprenticed to a carpenter in his youth, but come to London and founded a School of Anatomy in Windmill Street, and now like to turn all ideas up-side down; wherefore there be many that hate him, he having a damnable way of never Offering a Suggestion on matters Medico-Physical until he has proved it privately by Experiment beforehand; the which is Highly Exasperating to those that prefer to browse on the Windy Heights of Pure Discourse.

After the lecture, which was most instructive, to take a squint at the Hospital, to which one of its young gentlemen, a tall fellow with a pimply face and three-cornered hat, takes exception; likening us to Maggots crawling to a Fresh Cheese; at which George Blumenfield snorts and strikes him in the belly (he being too short to reach his face) and the tall youth's friends fall upon us, and we being hard pressed the other gentlemen of Doctor Urquehart's class to aid us, and a right merry fight ensues. Mr. Pope was trodden down and near throttled by two fellows and I to snatch the arm off a preparation of a Skeleton that stood near, and to beat them over the head with it; so that one was temporarily deprived of his wits, and Mr. Pope gets to his feet very fierce and throws off the other; and then more students hurrying out from class-rooms the medley became Very Strenuous; only we being possesesd by a Most Persistent and Obstinate Courage did force them back and back, catching up on our way very curious a Visiting Physician, who did cry Shame! Shame! until some wight wielding a cane did knock his wig over his eyes so that he was deprived of Speech. The Hospital Porter to fight us also, rushing out with a cudgel with which he did much damage, until Mr. Blumenfield snatches the Skull off the Skeleton and throws it between his legs very adroit; so that he crashed down like a wind-blown tree and was no more seen. I did catch sight of the yellow poll of Mr. St. Clair very valiant at the front using a tendon with a piece of muscle attached after the manner of a Spanish lassoo, and did join him, catching one fellow who sought to oppose me with a very clean Cross Buttock throw, so that he joined the Porter on the floor and was also no more seen. And so we fought, George Blumenfield crying joyous "Into your cheese you maggots!" until the press broke, and we not wishing to disturb the

Patients in the Wards, whom we could hear crying dismally in fear of a Riot and subsequent fire, did retire All Flushed with Victory; carrying with us the Tall Pimply Gentleman the cause of the trouble, whom we did throw into a Pond at the gates for the Healing of his Distemper; the Wig of the Physician, this upon Mr. Pope's cane; and the major portion of the breeches of the Porter, over whom Mr. Blumenfield had stumbled as we retired, and snatched off as Token.

March 21.

Doctor Urquehart very stern this morning, and to deliver a Homily on Manners, instead of a Lecture on Anatomy; interrupted by a messenger, who brought Two Missives; one a bill from the Governor's Secretary of St. George's Hospital for the following items:

One Wig for Doctor Ramsden, £3.

Eleven windows, broken, 30/–

One Anatomical, Osseous, preparation, ruined, £1.

One Anatomical, Muscular, preparation, ditto, £1. (The source of Mr. St. Clair's lassoo.)

One pair britches for Gate Porter, £2.

To damage to wits of same, £5.

One table deprived of leg, 10/–

Four Stools, broken beyond repair, £1.

Damage to walls and ceilings, £2. (From we presume one gentleman's nose having bled all over the wall, and Mr. Pope having thrown an ink-pot at the roof on departing.)

Wear and Tear to Nervous Composure of Patients, £10.

Five spittoons and a pot, cracked, £3.

Paint off three doors, 24/–

Split in panel of Anatomy room, 5/–

Loss of water and paint from gardeners tank in front garden, 11/–. (This being we suppose the pond into which we threw the pimply gentleman.)

Medicines for revival of two Hysterick Ladies, 3/–. (two fusty old faggots who were in the Porter's lodge when the fight commenced.)

TOTAL; £31.3.0.

At which the Doctor did first frown and then smile, saying that he would settle the matter for us for £10; this to be collected among us, adding that he hoped that we had had ten guineas worth of Fun, the which we assured him was the case, our brows being Laurel Bound with Victory; at which he did laugh outright, and looked strangely pleased.

The other letter more serious, though not more Impudent, being of all things a challenge to George Blumenfield from the tall youth with the pimples "He Being Wounded in That Tenderest Portion of A Man's Conscience His Honour; and, Trusting that His Aggressor of Yesterday at least Understood What was Due to a Gentleman, would Afford Him the Satisfaction of Personally Avenging the Slight put upon him" at which George Blumenfield smiles crookedly and turning to me asks "May he borrow my Small Sword?" and then requesting leave to quit the class from the Doctor, goes out to the messenger, and to send by him an answer to the pimply gentleman that he was At His Service; that as the Challenged Party he had chosen Swords; and that he would be with his seconds at the Leaping Hart that afternoon, and trusted that he would find the pimply gentleman's friends there to arrange The Meeting Place; and so returns; and we settle down again, and to Anatomise.

When we adjourned to the Tavern aforesaid we did find two gentlemen there very cold and haughty; and it was arranged that the Meeting was to take place at six o'the clock the next morning, at my suggestion in a secluded Walk that I knew of behind Marylebone Church; so that tomorrow, despite it being Sunday, I am to see my first affair of honour; and do pray that all will go well.

March 22.

Up betimes this morning and to the Meeting place appointed for the duel; took a stoup of milk and a piece of bread in the kitchen before setting forth, being most Confoundedly Low in my spirits; though this I could not understand, as it was not I who was to face Cold Steel. The morning perfect for the time of year; clear and sunny, with a frosty sparkle on the grass; few souls about save labourers and such going to work; found George Blumenfield and Mr. Pope there when I did arrive; Mr. St. Clair joined us after a few minutes; our adversaries already present, the pimply youth very Pale, but striving to Preserve a Composed Exterior; marred somewhat by a chattering of teeth that he did not seem able quite to control. Mr. Blumenfield almost indecently cheerful; whistling, and after my sword had been measured with that of the pimply youth's, suppling it in his fingers and making it whistle through the air; at which the chattering of the teeth of the Pimply Youth broke out afresh; and I to have a strange sudden notion that he was a Coward, and had been forced into this Rencontre by his friends. But Mr. St. Clair and one of the opposing seconds paced out a Stretch; and then the second cries out "Salute! Present!" and the two Duellists stood up on Guard their weapons crossed, that of the pimply youth's waving like an aspen, with the Vehemence of his Emotions. And then St. Clair calls out "Onset!" whipping out a sword of his own to strike up the blades when blood was shed.

Despite the freshness of the morning I did find my hands clammy as the blades flashed and twinkled in the sun; the pimply youth had found Courage from his Despair and was using the Length of his arm to hold off my friend. But this soon evaporated before the rapid lunges and thrusts of Mr. Blumenfield, and I to wonder where friend George had gained his knowledge of fencing; and in that second he darted in under the pimply youth's arm, swung his blade up and round, dashing aside his adversary's weapon, and brings his own home in the pimply youth's shoulder; at which that worthy squeals like a stuck pig. But George's foot slips, and the pimply youth with another squeal snarls and tries to slash open Mr. Blumenfield's head; prevented from this by Mr. St. Clair's blade, which by the Mercy of God caught it as the youth's sword descended; so that Mr. Pope and I cried "A Hit! A Hit!" and the tall youth's seconds "A Foul! Let them fight on!" which the Principals did, though not in the manner expected. For George Blumenfield grunts, drops his own blade, and wrests that of his opponent from his hand; and then with a Dex'trous twist jerks the pimply youth's head beneath his arm, and falls to belabouring him with the flat of his own sword. The youth's seconds rush to aid him, and we to prevent them; and we grappled and smote until suddenly George's instrument of Chastisement breaks, and he flings the pimply youth away from him; at which his seconds break off their fight with us and rush to succour him. Mr. Blumenfield very cool puts on his hat, cleans and sheathes his weapon, and hands it back to me; then walks over to the pimply youth, we following, to find his injury no more than a scratch that had scarce pierced the cloth of his coat. So George speaks to him kindly and the youth Blubs a bit with Pain and Mortification; and then we all shake hands and to breakfast in all Kindliness at the Leaping Hart; the pimply youth calling for wine and then asking friend George if he would take a glass with him, which George does, in all Friendliness; and so we sit down to beef and eggs, new bread, and tea, the jolliest souls in the City. Afterwards, feeling that a day so begun should not be allowed to pass without mark, we did hire a coach and drove down to Richmond; so that I have but lately returned; tired, and very thankful that a day with such Ominous Beginnings had ended so happily.

March 23.

At the Infirmary this day found the Wench's leg healing nicely the pus now decreasing daily so that the dressings are hardly wet and have only a little odour. The Dropsy's Belly filled up again so once more to Tap him; to make any Real progress I suspect that we should leave the Canula in, attaching a tap after the manner of bunging a cask. Another case of the Puerperal Fever in the Women's wards, the woman being taken early and Mr. Jamie coming hotfoot from an Autopsy to assist her; but all of no avail; the child born dead, an abortion with three legs, and the woman now far gone, with a racing pulse and in a coma. Did bleed her and threw up a Clyster; also inserted an Astringent Pessary, the Vulva being very foul; but fear that she will not last the night.

March 24.

On arrival home tonight did find a long letter from my uncle awaiting me, the contents of which have put any worries as to the Woman delivered last night being dead, right out of my head. The letter very moderate in tone, but to the effect that he had not been surprised by my communication, both for the reason that I had only a little capital, and also because whether I had much or little I was expected to run through it, having ever been careless where money was concerned. As to what I was expected to do in the future, he did assure me that if I were destitute he would at once take me in; but I being a surgeon had—here he quotes from an article in the Spectator written by Doctor Johnson—a passport to Fame all ready to my hand; and he did bid me therefore take my first step into the world and apprentice myself to some great Surgeon as his Assistant, either with or without applying first for a License to Surgeon's Hall; or endeavor to obtain a post as Apothecary in a Hospital where I might continue my studies whilst earning my bread and butter; the which letter did cause me to think furiously, I having half hoped—half expected—that he would offer me a post as his assistant, at least for a time; though I could now see that such a procedure would merely have staved off the inevitable moment when I should have to stand on my own feet and go out into the

Arena of Life to justify my life. And so, as I am weary enough with the disappointments of the day, and my head aches with thinking, will to finish this, and take up my candle and to bed.

March 25.

There being no work for me at Doctor Urquehart's, did to the Infirmary at mid-day, there to Anatomise the body of the Woman died yester morning from the Fever of Child-bed; and to find a degree of fever from which she could never have recovered; and so to the Lying-In Ward, there to find Mr. Rickard and Mr. Jamie busy with a Female that they had that morning discovered had a Polypoid growth in her Vagina; and she Expecting in a few days; and they to snare it with a wire loop on the end of a Bamboo rod, and to pass a ligature of silk about it that it may mortify and die before Parturition commences; and another woman gives a cry, so I to call Mr. Blumenfield and we to deliver her, a most trying and exhausting business, it being the middle of the afternoon before all was done; the two Hospital Physicians finishing their snaring and coming to watch us, but seeing that we did all right, to leave us to it; and I and George Blumenfield feeling most infernal dry to a tavern in Fleet Street, and later to the Leaping Hart, where we did find Mr. St. Clair and Mr. Pope; and an hour of pleasant discourse with them; and so home without having given se-

A London Hospital of the Eighteenth Century

(AFTER AN AQUATINT BY ROWLANDSON)

rious thought to my affairs, for which I do reprove myself.

March 26.

To walk in Tottenham field this morning, it being a fine day, and there to give grave thought to myself, my future, and my prospects. Did cogitate long and vigorously; then all at once, like the Opening of a Door, I did see my way clear before me. I thought all in a flash of the old mariner Ned, and his wond'rous tales of far-off seas, of those wonders that I had seen in the Museum of the Royal Society; and my mind was made up. I would join the Navy as a Surgeon; there I should surely find practice enough for my Art, and at the same time feed my mind with the Beauteous Creations of God—Sun-light over the Waters, Flying Fish and Porpoises, Mermaids and Tropic Isles. Thus my resolve made, and wond'ring a little that I should have been so perplexed when such a Land of Canaan lay before me, to turn my steps to Doctor Urquehart's house. There I did take the Doctor on one side, and told him all; and he to approve, saying kindly that I had been a diligent student, and that both for my uncle's sake and because he deemed me worthy, he would give me a Certificate that I must lay before my Lords of the Admiralty; adding that I was only just in time, for an Examination Board was sitting on April 3, this to inquire into the fitness of prospective surgeons to attend their Majesties Ships, the Board being composed both of Surgeons and Apothecaries; this examination would not, he told me, on account of the Certificate he would give me, be a difficult one; but I must beware of my answers in Physic, a sturdy knowledge not only of drugs but of Diet being required in one who far from land would hold the health of all the ship's company within his hands. And so to commend me in writing the which being sanded and sealed I did bear forthwith to the Offices of the Admiralty; and then in some excitement back to the Infirmary, there, alas, to find the woman George and I delivered very sick, with ominous pains in her belly; so in despair to bleed her, and blister the abdomen; and then the poor wench growing distracted in her wits did resolve at least to see that she had a quiet passing; and so, Mr. Blumenfield kindly declaring that he would watch with me, we did pass a Doleful Vigil, until at a quarter after nine at night she sank into that Coma which presages the End; and Mr. Rickard comes to us and touches us gently on the shoulders; and so we left her; and friend George and I to take a stoup of wine at the Leaping Hart, and I to tell him of all my resolve; for which he did commend me, saying though that he would Miss my ugly phiz infernally; and so home to our lodgings, where having written this I have come over Intolerably Drowsy.

March 27.

Went straightway to the Infirmary this morning, to equip myself with a closer acquaintance of the Materia Medica; there I did find that the woman with the Child-bed Fever was that moment sped, she having rallied at seven o'clock, and come to her senses, though she knew not where she was nor her circumstances; another Example of the Kindliness of God's Providence. The Dropsy better; the Squills do seem to be chasing the Humours from him and livening up his Absorbents. In the Pharmacy to discourse with Doctor Leeds upon those diseases peculiar to Mariners; especially that greatest scourge, the Scurvy, the which is due it would seem to the Acrimonious Salts with which the Blood becomes charged when the Body is exposed to the Saltness of the Sea. Doctor Leeds did say that many Treatments had been applied to it, all having the Idea that the salts in the blood must be neutralised by Acids; so that Vinegar, Lead Water, and Sulphuric Acid had been used; but he for his part preferred the Natural Acids of Fruit, especially those of the Orange and the Lemon; quoting the experiments of one Doctor James Lind, a Naval Surgeon, who had recently published a pamphlet On the Diseases of Europeans in Hot Climates, in which he showed that he had cured men of the scurvy by these means.

March 28.

Have been at the Infirmary nigh all day, reading up my drugs, and in the Authorities on the Causation of Disease.

March 29.

At church; to pray to God most humbly and fervently for guidance and strength in all I am to do.

April 1.

Have not written in this Journal these few days, nor shall until my Examination be past; being anxious to preserve a Tranquillity of Spirits; the which I am not so likely to do if I sit up writing late at night. Have wrote to my uncle acquainting him of my purpose; so now my boats be burned behind me.

April 3.

Have but now returned from Examination Hall, and my wits still in a flummox. Was up betimes this morning with an infernally dry mouth, and to shave and dress myself with all care and decency; and then after forcing some breakfast down, to Examination Hall; where I did find a crowd already waiting and more arriving; and the Porter to glance at his list and to inform me that I had two hours to wait. So did seat myself, but the doleful converse of those about me did so depress me that after an hour I got to my feet, snatched up my hat, and rushed into the streets; where I wandered about aimlessly until my time appointed; then back to the Hall, and into the Examination Room, feeling More Peculiar than I ever dreamt was possible; my mouth dry, my hands clammy, and my mind Tight Bound with a Strange Numbness. The room very lofty, but barely furnished; five gentlemen in imposing wigs did sit about a table, one in the centre, the most stupid looking of all, had some chain of office about his neck. There were laid out on the table on my right hand sundry bottles of drugs, and bundles of medicinal plants; and on the table to my left were some bones, surgical instruments, and some anatomical preparations, some in spirits in bottles, some dry, and one or two wax models; and I at the sight of them did feel as I suppose a Rabbit feels when it puts its nose out of its burrow to find the Terriers waiting outside.

The stupid gentleman in the middle glares at me Very Stern, and then consults some papers on the table before him, and looking at me again, says that he was glad to see that Doctor Urquehart spoke well of me; as though he was surprised thereat, the which did not help me to regain my Composure. And then one with a pock-marked face seated at the drugs on my right did request me to come over to him, which I did and he and the Doctor or Apothecary with him —I know not which he was—did pelt me with questions concerning Drugs and Their Use; I managing to hold them off, till the pock-marked one snatched up a bundle of dried leaves and waving them under my nose did demand to know what they were; at which I gaped at him, not having any notion of what they might be, confused even more in my wits by Catching the eye of the President very gloomy. And then he to tell me they were Plantain leaves, at which I did reproach myself, having seen them in the Infirmary; though his hard to recognise, being brown and very dusty and broken. And so they having made a Breach in my Citadel did pour through it, questioning me on divers drugs and compounds the most of which I had never even heard of.

After they had toyed with me for some quarter of an hour, the President did ring a little bell, and then requests me to pass over to those examining on Anatomy and Surgery; and I did move to seat myself before them, certain in my own mind that I was already failed. But one of the two new Examiners—I learnt after that his name was Mr. Sainthill—did glance at me shrewdly, and murmur something to his companion; and then leans across the table to me, and says much to my surprise and comfort "A Country Lad, eh? Ever hunted?" and on my nodding, smiles and says "Well, now, you're going to take a Jump. Your horse is all right. Take your time, and think what you're about!" the which friendliness did strangely give me back my wits, so that I answered him and his companion to their complete satisfaction; being examined largely, by the grace of God, on Anatomy with which I am well conversant, and on Amputations and the Puerperal Fever, both subjects to which I had given much thought. And so Mr. Sainthill looks up at the President, and nods; and that worthy rings the bell, and the Porter comes in, and I am requested to wait in an anteroom adjoining; which I do, and then after some twenty minutes more the Porter comes in again to conduct me to the Examination Room; where to my Great Surprise and Delight the President informs me that I have satisfied the examiners, and hands me a Diploma from the Society of Apothecaries and a smaller certificate certifying that I be a true Chirurgeon; and I catch the eye of Mr. Sainthill smiling and nodding, and I to realise that it was due to his good offices that I was now possessed of a License; moreover I was informed that I was appointed Surgeon's Mate on a ship of sixth rate the Lancaster, now lying at Blackstakes; and a further message in writing to this effect. Then the President very solemn gives me a small admonishment on the Honour now bestowed on me and the Importance of never bending my Professional Knowledge to mean ends; to which I duly assented; and then he unexpectedly smiles like the sun coming out from behind a cloud and wishes me God Speed; and so with my head All Giddy out into the street and so home to

Mr. Hunt's, the worthy man. He and his wife, yea, and the serving wench as pleased with my success as if I had been their own son; and so to eat, and then to write this; which being finished, I must indite a letter to my uncle, telling him of all that has befallen; and this done I will to my chamber, there to fall to my knees to thank Almighty God for all His Goodness to me, not forgetting this late mercy of Mr. Sainthill, whose name I shall ever hold in Grateful Remembrance.

April 4.

Up betimes and to Doctor Urquehart's house, there to acquaint him and all my friends with my News; at which they did all fall to congratulating me, and I near to tears with realisation of all their friendliness. And so I took a farewell of them all, giving the Doctor's huge serving-man a small fee. Then to my Hospital for the last Time, and to take adieu of Messrs. Jamie and Rickard, and Doctor Leeds, who did admonish me to remember all that he told me of the treatment of those diseases peculiar to Mariners and the Oceans. Dined at a tavern alone, not having the Heart or the Guineas to join my friends as they suggested for a last Gathering at the Leaping Hart. So home, and to study my accounts, they revealing me to have even less Capital than I had suspected. There is someone knocking at my host's door; I hear voices that are familiar. My friends have arrived, Mr. George Blumenfield and Mr. St. Clair, Mr. Pope, yes, and the pimply gentleman and a friend of his from St. George's Hospital. They are now ascending the stairs and calling to me; so no more will be written in this my Journal tonight.

April 5.

Was very late home last night, having passed the hours until Dawning in All Friendliness with those that came for me last night. I did find on descending that not only were my especial friends and the two gentlemen from St. George's Hospital gathered, but in the street without several others of Doctor Urquehart's class; and we did all repair to the Devil Tavern in Fleet Street, where the good fellows had caused a Great Supper to be spread in my honour, with much wine and other liquors, having for afterwards taken a box at the Haymarket Theatre. At the Tavern we did feast right royally, the pimply youth from St. George's Hospital proving to have a rare turn of wit, and making on behalf of the Art Of Medicine a mighty fine speech, in which he spoke of the Universal Brotherhood of Physicians, they all whether German, Dutch, French, Spanish, yea even Arabic, working together for One Aim the Amelioration of Suffering Amongst Mankind; and made reference to that "Brother and Friend" now present who was so shortly to venture out and Sail the Wide Tempestuous Seas; hoping that that brother in all his Wanderings would never forget that Universal Brotherhood of which he had spoken and would foster it by His Friendliness and Help to all the foreign Physicians and Surgeon's he might meet; at which loud cheers from the company, and then George Blumenfield gets to his feet and says how sorry he will be to miss that Brother from amongst their company (this with an eye on me) saying how he esteems him for his Genuine Worth, Stout Heart, and Nobility of Character; and then snatching up his glass commences to sing an old Cavalier Air:

Horse have I, and a goodly sword,
And the fairest maid for mistress.
Yet grant me still the gift of a friend
Who will stand through Weal and Woe, etc.

At which they all jumped to their feet and with glass in air joined him, so that the room rang with their voices, and then when it was ended sat them down again hurling away their glasses in the fire with a great noise, calling on me for Response. So, strangely moved with Emotion so that my knees shook and I had difficulty in controlling my voice, I to my feet and thanked them perhaps haltingly but God knows with all Sincerity for their Goodness and Kindness; which ended more loud cheers and one gentleman disappears beneath the table. He being found and restored to his Status Quo one or two other gentlemen did essay various songs, among those that I remember being "Oh, Mistress mine, where Art thou roaming?" and that pretty thing of Colonel Lovelace's, "I could not love thee dear so much, Loved I not honour more—" these being thought especial appropriate for me, as one departing to the Wars. And then we did repair to the Theatre, and I was struck by further kindness of my friends; for on the reckoning being called for, they would none of them agree that I should pay my share, and the pimply gentleman asks me with a smile and a mock seriousness whether I wished to fight a duel with him; at which all laugh, and friend George slips his arm through that of the pimply youth's, and his other arm through mine, and so singing a Catch we out into the street and to the Theatre.

And I must confess that I remember little of what we saw there. It was, I do know, a most Grim and Horrific Tragedy, an uncle murdering his Niece in the very first Act; and then her Ghost did appear in the Second Scene, to haunt the said uncle; at which Ghost Mr. Pope did make pretence to be Greatly Affrighted, swooning so that the pimply youth and friend George made much ado to restore him, and great noise thereat. Then the Wicked Uncle, still not repenting of His Misdeed, did make a bargain with a Rogue of a Highway Man to shoot the Spark of his niece; and we did see the Highway Man and the Uncle meet at a Crossroads at Night beneath a moon; and at the sight of the robber one of Doctor Urquehart's young gentlemen did cry lustily for the Watch, saying that he should straightway be apprehended, and leaning over the box, did lose his wig, it slipping from his head to the stage; and much noise thereat from the surrounding audience, he finally swathing his head in the curtain of the box and going to sleep; and peace being Temporarily Established the play did proceed. The uncle did slip away, and the Spark appears very gallant, and the Highway Man pounces upon him, and they fought most desp'rate, the Spark being taken by surprise and being Hard-pressed; only he calling on "Belinda! Belinda!" to aid him (said Belinda being the wench foully murdered in the first Act) the ghost of same appears; at which moment Doctor Urquehart's young gentleman did awake and feeling his head chilly without his Wig, snatches Mr. Pope's cane, and leans over the edge of the box to recover it. Only being foxed with wine he did catch instead the Ghost's Robe and flicks it off; and it was revealed as no Ghost, but a real woman, a pretty little doxy clad in naught but her shift and a pair of white stockings; at which the commoner folk in the galleries did shout, and some gentry in the box opposing to cheer lustily.

The Actors however were greatly enraged, and the Highway Man comes across the stage and shakes his fist very ferocious at the young gentleman; and he rises to his feet to Make a Leg and Offer Apologies to the Doxy, and straightway tumbles out of the box on to the stage; at which more shouts from the audience, and the Highway Man rushes up and seizing him by the seat of his Breeches, hove him into the Orchestra; and much damage thereby to a 'Cello and a Fiddle. Mr. St. Clair gives a Hurroo! and jumps on the stage also and squaring up to the Highway Man did give him a Buffet that sent him flying back into the Scenery, with such force that the Moon did fall down, it being naught but a Lantern suspended from the Roof. And it is from this point that my recollections grow Misty, for a Mighty Hubbub Began, the Spark running to the help of the Actor Highway Man and receiving a second buffet from Mr. St. Clair that sent him to join his friend; and George Blumenfield jumps on the stage to reassure the Doxy, and putting his arm round her did receive a scratch that furrowed his face; and then the audience rose in Fury and did set upon us, some of the Gentlemen in the box opposite coming to our aid, and thereby being attacked in turn; and the Carpenters and Workmen of the Theatre did rush out from behind the scenery to aid the audience, so that we and the gentry were presently thrust forth into the street; I having one clear picture of Doctor Urquehart's young gentleman snatching his Wig, placing it upon his head All Awry, and then defending himself vigorously with the remnants of the

'Cello upon which he had fallen; and did afterwards meet him in the gutter, his fine coat all Dusty and his Breeches torn from the vehemence of the Highway Man, but mighty pleased to have got his Wig back; though this from some one having emptied or broken a bottle of wine over it was naught but a Towsled Rag. And so, being prevented from returning to the Theatre we did join the Gentry, and with them to a Low Gaming Room in a street near the hamlet of St. Giles-in-the Fields; and I knowing naught of cards, did slip away from thence in the small hours and so home.

I awoke this morning with a vile taste in my mouth and a head as heavy as a Copper, but wishing to attend Church, for the last time perhaps in London town, I did rise and with the Hunts to hear Mr. Hardy discourse on the Sermon on the Mount; and to walk with them in Tottenham fields after. Tomorrow must see my departure to enter among strangers upon a way of life of which I have no more idea than of the Mogul's court. Have said naught to my friends or to the Hunts, but after settling my reckonings I shall be left with barely a guinea to enter my new profession, and did wonder today how I might pay my coach-fare to Blackstakes, this lying some way out from London city; being I have learnt a roadstead in North Kent in the river Medway above Sheerness. After some thought I did decide to pawn my watch. So tonight I have taken leave of my friends—they have become more to me than mere Host and Hostess—and have presented my fine Small Sword to Mr. Hunt, he being much pleased with it, also have given his wife a present of a laced Cap to wear about the house; and the serving wench two of my last shillings. And now, this being wrote, to bed.

Part Two

AT SEA

I

April 7.

Did not enter in this Journal last night, being All Mazed with the Strangeness of my surroundings; and for that matter, am still. Rose betimes yester morn, and after breaking my fast and taking a final leave of the Hunts, took my valise in hand, and repaired to a Pawn Shop; having with difficulty prevented Mr. Hunt from coming to see me off by telling him I was going to the Hospital first; for which small peccadilloe may God forgive me. The man who owned the Pawn Shop naught but a Rogue, and would not give me more than two guineas for my watch; with which I had to be content. Then on to the Coaching House where to my Surprise I did find Mr. Blumenfield, Mr. Pope, and Mr. St. Clair waiting for me, they having come to give me a Send-Off. And the coach waiting in the Yard, I did climb to the outside seat that I had taken, and the Guard blew his horn, and we drove off, my friends cheering and Mr. Pope calling after me to "Bring Him back a Mermaid!" at which the other passengers on the coach were much Amused. The day fine, and I rather glad thereat, for I was somewhat downcast in my spirits.

But I took pleasure after a while in the ride, and could look about me with enjoyment, the country just commencing Spring Time and the buds showing on the trees. But when we had covered scarce half our journey, and were out on the first marshes, the Off Leader shies at a hen flying across the road, and before we had scarce time to think what was afoot, the Coach lurches, and then tumbles over into a ditch, the road being soft with mud at that point. The ditch was deep so none was hurt bad; but two women inside began to scream most piercing, being badly shook in their wits; and one gentleman was thrown clean off the roof into a hedge and was hauled out by Yr. Obdt. Servant and the Guard all abroad in *his* Wits.

The horses were in an aweful Tangle, kicking and struggling so that it was as much as the Coachman could do to calm them; the Guard and a gentleman in a bottle green coat went to aid him, and after some twenty minutes and much hard swearing of Oaths the horses were got free of their harness and taken up on to the road; when it was found that the bay leader was lame in the near fore, and I to bathe the swelling then coming up with water from the ditch, and at the Guard's suggestion to bleed the beast also at the neck: the Guard observing in a Hoarse Whisper that I might bleed the Females also, they still screaming faintly at regular intervals, like he informed me the Watch Guns of the Revenue Men. The coach was wedged firm between the banks of the ditch, one wheel being out of sight, and the Coachman and the Guard both agreed that it was probably cracked.

We did all get together and endeavour to push the coach free, but its weight was against us, so that after some sweating we did desist, and turn to helping the ladies from within; they vowing that their bones were all broke to little pieces and they could not stir, no, not for the Judgement day, and more to the same effect; at which the Guard loses patience, and wrenching the door open grabbed what his hand found and hauled the first lady on to the road, her screams breaking out anew as he slipped an arm round her waist to prevent her slipping into the ditch. The other lady within also began to scream at this Brutality of the Guard, and protested that she would not be hauled out like a sack of Malt, and began to stab with her parasol so that the Guard took off his hat and scratched his head in Bewilderment. Only the gentleman in the bottle green coat puts him aside, and bending as elegantly as he might under the circumstances, removes his head-gear and inserts his poll within the coach; at which a fresh burst of screams from the lady, dying away most strangely as the gentleman, a pleasant looking fellow enough, says "that he begs her humblest apologies for Discommoding her, but the position of the coach being Somewhat insecure, Might he have the Honour to assist her to the Road?" this with a very winning smile; at which the lady goes all of a flutter, says she really doesn't know—perhaps the coach is insecure—it might be as well to alight—if the gentleman will excuse her deshaibillé—she is mortified to find herself in such straits—she is but a poor helpless Woman—if the gentleman perhaps would take pity on her—if the gentleman could—and the gentleman with another smile *does,* and hands her very gently to the road, she giving a squeak at seeing the empty ditch beneath the coach step and clinging to his arm, looking slyly up at her Preserver with a most arch smile; then when set on her feet beside the other decides to exercise the Prerogative of Her Sex to have the Vapours, and the other not to be outdone joins her, and they both go off in the Hystericks; at which the guard runs to the ditch, fills his hat with water, and running back again, was about to Throw It All Over Both of Them; only again is put aside by the gentleman in the bottle green coat who falls to one knee beside the lady he had helped out of the coach and fondling her hand murmurs Endearments to her, and I to assist the other Female. At which, she finding that no other gentleman comes to *her* aid, and the wench with the gallant not desiring to lose any chance of Romance, they both came round as suddenly as they had gone off; and I began to hunt in my valise for my Iv'ry Handled Lancets, with intent to bleed the gentleman thrown from the coach top; which I did, he becoming quite Sane thereby, and thanking me heartily for my Timely Aid.

An argument arises between the Coachman and the Guard as to what should be done next; the road being deserted and it imperative that Someone go for Help; but the Guard refusing to leave his Mails, and the Coachman his horses; it finally being settled that another gentleman, a Farmer, should take one of the team and ride off for assistance; which he did, and the Coachman to suggest that we passengers should walk on to the next Posting House; but the ladies showing signs of Hystericks at this idea, we did all stay, not helped thereby by a fine drizzle that began to fall; which did make us all miserable, except the wag in the bottle green coat, to whom it gave fresh opportunities for gallantry. After nigh two hours the Farmer returns with fresh horses and Assistance, and the coach was dragged out of the ditch and the team harnessed afresh; only, that wheel which had hung in the ditch being thought insecure, it was decided that only the ladies should ride within, and the team proceed at a walk. So we set off, one lady sulking, the other not caring at all as the gentleman in the bottle green coat was walking outside clasping her hand through the window, she all enveloped in his cape and fair enough to look at, as I think the little rogue well knew, being dark and petite, her curls shown up against the green collar of his cape.

It took us an hour more to reach the Posting House, and we were glad enough when we reached it to find Mine Host had prepared a meal both of hot and cold meats, with Tea for the ladies, and Wine and Ale for the gentlemen. There were sausages and eggs and ham, with pork-pies and brawn, and a side of beef, with a crusty new loaf and salt and fresh butter, and as there was moreover a roaring fire we were all greatly comforted. There was another coach in the yard, but this had to be prepared, and it was past dusk when we once more took our seats, and gone seven before I alighted at Blackstakes. This naught but a cottage and an ale house, from which rose a most noisy chorus. The coach rumbled away almost before I had alighted and feeling most Vilely Low in Spirits I did stand looking about me wondering what to do.

The rain had ceased, but the marshes were all covered with a low mist in which the coach lamps were speedily lost. I knocked at the Ale House door and receiving no answer entered, to find as thick a fog within as out, only that within doors was caused by the mingled fumes of a smoky fire and the coarsest of tobacco. The place was full of sailors, the landlord sitting in their midst, and one of the seamen with a girl (I found after to be his daughter) upon his knee. They were bawling some Sea Chanty as I entered, but on my coming into the room they did all cease and gazed at me as though I was some strange wonder risen from their Seas. Addressing the landlord, I asked if he could tell me aught of the Sixth Rate Vessel Lancaster, where she was lying, whether at Dock side or in the roads; but at this the fellow with the girl on his knee puts her to the ground with a "Cheerily, lass!" and steps up to me, enquiring civilly enough what my business with that ship might be. He was a brawny fellow, with a mass of close-cropped curls, better dressed than his companions, in white linen shorts, woollen stockings, and heavy shoes; a striped shirt and a thick blue coat; and a silver whistle hung from a lanyard about his neck. He spoke as one having some authority, and I told him that I was newly appointed Surgeon's Mate to the Lancaster; on which he roars out "Lads! Here's our new sawbones!" and then offering me a sinewy hand all stained with tar, adds "Shake hands, my bully, with Ned Tollit, bosun of the Lancaster!" and as I hesitated, says again, "Come shake, lad! We're all glad to welcome our new shipmate!" and gives my hand a squeeze that nigh crushed the bones in it. I asked him how I was to get on ship, but he informs me that the sailors there gathered were my only means of getting aboard, the ship lying out some distance in the roads, and no wherryman would venture out in the mist. He told me also that very few officers were then present, most of them being away and joining the ship at Portsmouth in two days; only a Lieutenant in charge, and he ashore, so that there would be no one to report to until the morning.

"Come and sit ye down, chum!" says Ned, throwing a great arm round my shoulders. "There is naught to worry ye. We will take ye with us when we go, and Ned Tollit will show you your quarters!" and thus constrained I joined the company, feeling very strange amongst such fellows, whose bronzed faces and tattooed arms spoke of the Hazardous lives they led. But I found them although rough the kindliest of fellows; each one of them was anxious to shake my hand and force drink on me and so make me feel at Ease; and after the worthy bosun had insisted on my drinking a glass of rum with him to celebrate my arrival, I found my Lowness of Spirits quite gone; and learnt the words of sundry Sea-Songs, so that when they at last rose to go I already felt myself one of them.

We left the Ale house and walked for some few minutes until we reached the shore, where we found the ship's boat drawn up; and the worthy Ned tumbled me into it and the seamen pushed off, and he took a place beside me in the sternsheets to direct us. And so we reached the Lancaster, she looming up sudden out of the mist after the sailors had pulled for some quarter of an hour, and I to marvel how they found their way, until Ned Tollit points out to me the tips of her masts sticking from the top of the fog-bank. She carried two riding lights, lanterns slung from spars, but no one answered Ned's hail, and he fell to cursing the Watch something to marvel at, saying that the Lubbers had belike Gone and Turned in, there being no one to Keep them Alert; and so lets out a Howl that nigh split my ear-drums, and gets in response a very faint cry; and as we slipped along the ship's side a seaman appears at the rail above us and throws a rope, and Ned falls to cursing him again. I was by that time Most Infernally Fatigued, and had only time to note the single row of gun-ports before Ned pushes a rope into my hand and gives me a Heave that near scattered my brains on the trap of one of the gun-ports aforesaid; and so I scrambled somehow to the deck, and was gaped at by the Watch as though I was King Neptune himself come aboard; and then Ned climbs over beside me, and leads me forward to a cabinn beneath the gun-deck just abaft the Fore-Mast; the Mast driving down to the bowels of the ship right through my cabbinn, its bulk forming as support for the door and a shelf on which was placed, inside a wooden rack, a large wood chest. There was a bunk behind it, and a swivel chair, and that was all the furnishing, the room being small so that I could scarce stand upright in it, and have to be careful in stretching my arms that I do not knock the skin off my knuckles against the walls.

In front of my door was a round space, with an alley running across from one side of the ship to the other; two ladders rose from this alley to the deck above; and Ned explains that the round space is the Cock-Pit to which the wounded and sick are brought, and that the alley leads to a magazine and the sailor's quarters in the Forecastle (Pronounced—Foc'sle). I put my valise on the bunk and remarked smiling to Ned that my quarters were small but cosy, and that the ship seemed stout enough; to which he gave a great bellow of Laughter, and says in the affectionate manner of which a Man will speak of his Mistress "She was a damned Old Baggage, and like to go to the bottom on her Next Voyage—but there, he didn't give a Rush!" and then touches his forelock and begs to be excused; and I left to myself, to unpack my box, and climb into my bunk; where despite the Strangeness of my new bed, I straightway fell asleep; the last sound I heard was Ned Tollit's voice calling on the seamen to make the boat fast.

The first sound that awoke me this morning was the same Ned Tollit's voice and a rumbling noise on deck; and I rose in haste, and was half dressed when there was a knock at the door and opening it I found an urchin with an ewer of hot water, very acceptable to shave with; and then I made my way on deck, where I found friend Ned conducting three sailors who were washing down the decks.

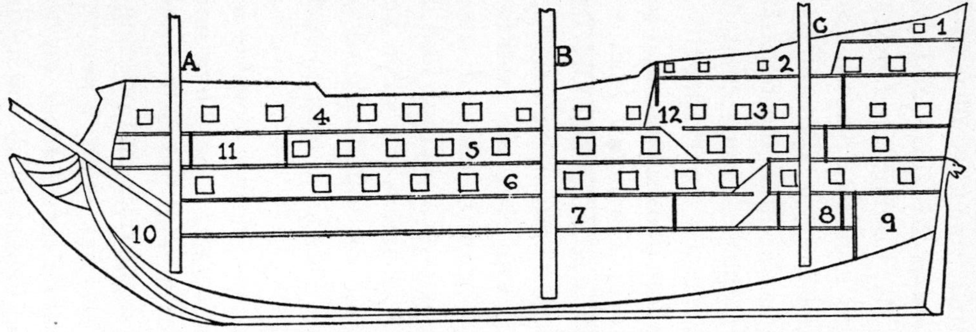

A Diagrammatic Representation of an Eighteenth-Century Ship of War

A. Fore mast. B. Main mast. C. Mizzen mast. 1. Poop. 2. Quarter-deck. 3. Half-deck. 4. Spar-deck. 5. Main, second, or upper deck. 6. First or lower gun-deck. 7. Orlop-deck. 8. After-cockpit. 9. After powder-magazine. 10. Forward powder-magazine. 11. Galley. 12. Main-hatchway. (Reconstructed from an illustration in SEA LIFE IN NELSON'S TIME by John Masefield, and from a longitudinal section of a seventy-four-gun ship in ELEMENS DE L'ARCHITECTURE NAVALE, by M. Duhamel Du Monceau, Paris, 1752. Reproduced from ANNALS OF MEDICAL HISTORY, Paul B. Hoeber, Inc., 1925.)

The mist of the night before had cleared and I had a fine view of the distant marshes and the sea all sparkling in the early morning sunlight; the crying of the gulls and the chanting of the three sailors blending curiously to make a Harmonious Whole. Ned comes up to me, and enquires "How I found my new Dock?" and then informs me that Breakfast was awaiting me in the Saloon and directs me thither, where food was served me by a very old man whose age I found on enquiry to be eighty-two years, he having served in His Majesty's Navy since a boy, and seen thereby more sea-fights than he could count. The food very plain and somewhat coarse, but plentiful; cold meat, bread and butter, with the choice of Ale or Coffee as drink; I did choose Coffee, having had enough of Liquor the night previous; and so I finished, and on deck again.

The Lancaster is a well found ship, being newly built; and carrying 24 guns, to wit, twenty nine-pounders on the Main Gun Deck and four three pounders, two on the quarter deck and two on the forecastle. Her burthen is 504 tons, and her complement 172 men fighting strength. These facts I learnt later, as I had scarce glanced around me with keen interest when Ned Tollit approaches and knuckling his forehead asks "Would I be good enough to see one-two men who were sick?" to which of course I agreed, and so down to the Cockpit, where I found three sailors gathered. A glance at these showed me that my first cases as a Ships Chirurgeon were naught serious; one man suffering from a Surfeit of Drink, which I eased with a purge and acid drink; another a boil at the back of his neck, which I lanced; and the third an Exfoliation of the skin of his ear very tender, which I eased with an ointment that I had with me in my valise; there being I discovered some drugs in a wooden chest screwed to the wall of the cockpit, but these few in number and of poor quality. The sailors did not seem worried in anyway about their Trifling Complaints, and I think had come to see what manner of man I was; by the time I had done with the last quite a number of their companions were gathered about, and all seemed somewhat surprised that I took so much trouble with them, and to talk with them. Then the Lieutenant comes aboard, and I to his cabin to report; he a young spark mighty supercilious, who informs me that the Lancaster is captained (or commanded it seems is the correct term) by the Honourable John Hamilton; as though Royalty were coming aboard at Portsmouth; then seeing that I was not duly impressed the Spark gets up saying he had work to do and would shortly have some work for me; and goes up on deck and calls Ned Tollit, and Ned falls to blowing his silver whistle and six seamen run up all armed with cutlasses, and then they and Ned and the Lieutenant get into the boat and it pulls away for the shore; and I fill a Pipe of Tobacco—a habit I have newly acquired—and seating myself in the bows on a coil of rope, whence I had a view over the length of the ship, sat and smoked and Mused on all these new changes in my life. The sun was then quite warm, and the morning passed very Agreeably, I finding much to Intrigue my Interest and Excite my Curiosity; I did admire on the one hand the manner in which the Masts and Spars of this ship my new home towered to the sky, very graceful; and on the other the Grim Utility of the brass carronades on the forecastle beside me; being thereby reminded of the Old Stave:

Bold were the Men who on the Ocean first
Spread the new Sails, when Ship-wreck was the worst;
More dangers NOW from MAN alone we find
Than from the Rocks, the Billows, and the Wind...

and from that fell to regarding the Sea that Dimpled and Rippled so near me; whence rising from my seat I could see trailing from the ship side the Long Streamers of the Sea Weeds, with shoals of tiny fish playing amongst their Forest Recesses: marvelling at their nimbleness and wondering what Quaint Structures might thereat be revealed by the Microscope of Mr. Kelly.

Dinner was served at twelve by the old cook in the same Saloon in which I had breakfasted; and after it I slept awhile, and awoke to find Ned and the Lieutenant still absent, and to wonder what they were at; and so to pass the time to enter all this in my Journal. As dusk was falling however they returned; I had then gone on deck to take the Air, when my attention was catched by sundry seamen running to the side all laughing and cheering; and crossing to that Landward side, did observe the boat returning, as yet little more than a speck, but a speck that swelled and grew small in manner Amazing; whence I did see as it approached that this Systole and Diastole was caused by three New Strangers in the boat, they seemingly very Restless; and so as the boat drew still nearer I did see that these were three likely lads empressed by the Lieutenant and his sailors, they having gone ashore to recruit seamen, being armed as these Press Gangs are greatly feared and hated by the landsmen. One man was quieter than the others, but his two companions were Wrestling and Fighting so that every minute I expected to see the boat overturn; and when it was still some distance from the ship one Valiant Rogue suddenly jumps up and springs into the Sea; only as he swum past the boat's stern, the Lieutenant snatches off the Tiller Bar and crowns him with it, so that he was Stunned and like to have sunk, only that one of the Sailors pushes his oar under his arms and so holds him until other seamen lean over and drag him once more into the boat. And so they were brought to the Ship's side, the

Lieutenant cursing because Salvaging the wight had soaked his Breeches, one of the Impressed men crying aloud on them to Have Mercy on him for the sake of his young wife, she seemingly very sick, one all wet and insensible, and the third Quiet with the Resignation of Despair; and all three very bloody and bruised, as were most of their captors.

But what was my Amazement to recognise in the Resigned Man my friend the Consumptive of Infirmary Hall! He having grown heavy with flesh and his face rosy so that I scarce knew him. As Ned Tollit hoisted him to the deck I took his hand and asked him if he knew Me; at which he stares at me agape, and then his face lights up, and he falls to his knees, clasping my hands, and saying that he thanked God for having sent him one friend; at which I did see some of the sailors glancing curious at him; only the Lieutenant comes up swearing and kicks him to his feet saying, "Get below, dog!" and so he and the others were hustled off to the seamen's quarters, the stunned man being brought into the Cockpit for my attention. He was then coming to his wits, and on my bleeding him recovered them completely, and so I to tell Ned to get him to a bunk out of way of the Lieutenant, he being much bruised having evidently made a fight for it, and would be little good for anything till he had had a night's rest. I supped with the Lieutenant in the

Saloon, never speaking as his manner was very offensive; and so after another Pipe to my cabbinn, where finishing this I will Turn In, as they say in the Navy.

April 10.

Today we lie outside the Harbour of Portsmouth. Early yester morning we weighed anchor with much cheery noise, the Carpenter seating himself on the capstan and playing a tune on his fiddle to which the seamen spun the bars, they all singing the refrain

Oh, there was a little drummer and he loved a one eyed cook,
And he loved her, Oh, he loved her though she had a cock-eyed look,
With her one eye in the pot, and the t'other up the chimney,
With a Bow-wow-wow, Fal-lal the dow-a-diddy, etc.

Then when the Anchor had come up all muddy and green and dripping with water and been safely Catted, the Lieutenant, pacing up and down the quarter Deck with his glass under his arm, very fierce barks an order and the Quartermaster shouts, and Ned Tollit blows his whistle, and the seamen run to the Halliards and Swarm out along the Spars with a nimbleness that did amaze me. The carpenter struck up another tune, and a tall sailor with a fine melodious though untrained voice strikes up:

Oh, blow the man down, bullies, blow the man down!

To which the sailors did all respond as they hauled at the Halliards

To me, Way-ay, blow the man down!

Then the tall seaman again:

Oh, blow the man down, bullies, blow him away!

and his messmates:

Oh! Gimme some time to blow the man down!

And so through sundry verses until the sails bellied out and, the wind being fair, we set off to the Open Sea; and I mighty excited, and to walk about until outside the bar the ship began to rise and fall very disturbing; so that when dinner came I had no stomach for my Meat, and in the Afternoon felt that Death was surely approaching me; but was somewhat cheered by the worthy Ned, who visited me with a bowl of soup and informed me that this Upheaval of Man's Economy was but the price paid by all to Neptune; and so I managed to compose myself for sleep, and was this morning fairly recovered, though still somewhat Queasy. The wind continuing fair, we made reasonable progress, and this afternoon came in sight of our Harbour, anchoring outside in the Roads amongst a great profusion of ships of all sizes and callings; round bellied merchantmen, clippers from the Indie Seas, and Naval vessels also, gun boats, sloops, fourth and third raters, and one mighty Line of Battle Ship called Ned informs me the Ramillies, carrying one hundred guns of all sizes. Most of our ship's company have gone ashore, including to my relief the Lieutenant (His name by the way is Mr. Duhamel), but I have elected to stay aboard, my legs still being weak. Shall to bed as soon as this is wrote, though it is only just gone nine of the clock by the ship's bell.

April 11.

Today we have lain in the roadstead, the motion of the ship being somewhat erratic, but to my delight no Illness to me thereby; the which I take as fair proof that I have now acquired my Sea Legs. This morning did attend sundry wights in the Cockpit, and meeting with the Consumptive did talk with him awhile; he informing me that he had greatly benefited by his sojourn with his uncle, this worthy determined to get some return for his Hospitality before his nephew died, and so getting him up early in the morning and setting him to work about the farmyard and in the fields by day; teaching him much about sheep, the which was the Consumptive's undoing; for going down to the country near Blackstakes to report on a Flock, he was dining in an Alehouse when the Pressgang breaks in; at which he being near the door was promptly secured though one wight with him jumps through a window and so escapes. He is now seemingly quite cured of his Distemper; says that he has no cough, and, curiously, that he has now no desire to spin poetry; the which Rhyming I take it is one of those devices employed by Thoughtful Nature to distract the Sufferers Wits from his Complaint. His two companions are now resigned to their lot, though the one with the wife Broods Much, and Ned Tollit keeps a wary eye on him lest he break out Frantic and throw himself overboard. The ship very busy today, some Officers coming aboard, the most very foxed; and we have also taken aboard a Great Quantity of Stores, Cags of Gunpowder and Flour, Crates with Vegetables and some Conies and Chickens, Sail Cloth, and sundries for the Carpenter, Casks of Water and Pickled Meat, Cartridges and Buckets of Cannon Balls and Small Arm Shot for the Musketeers; so that the deck has nigh been invisible beneath their load, and the sailors running hither and thither I have spent most of my time beneath Deck. This night the Commander has come aboard to see that all is progressing satisfactorily. I have not yet met him, and shall see but little of him, for as the Jove of this Aquatic Olympus he lives the most of his sea-life in his Great Cabbinn in the stern.

April 12.

Sunday, and did see our Commander, he taking a short service in the middle of the morning, the Chaplain being sick ashore. The service very impressive, the men all gathered in the Waist with their Officers, the Bosun, the Gunner and Gunner's Mate, and the Quartermasters standing in front, with the First, and Second Lieutenants and the Midshipmen standing in a little group in front of them; the Marines and the First and Second Marine Officers with their Musketeers facing the Lieutenants and the Commander and the First Marine Officer on the Poop, with the Carpenter standing by with his fiddle, and the Master to con the ship that naught might go awry whilst we paid our duties to God. Yr. Obdt. Servant stood with the Midshipmen, and had thereby a fine view of our Commander, he a tall elderly man with something of a crack in his voice. The day being fine all passed off well, and we could hear the singing from the rest of the Fleet. Being Sunday little work was done save that essential to securing the ship, the men lying about on deck mending their clothes and shaving, and the carpenter with his fiddle was greatly in request, there being much singing. More sailors arrived tonight, and also the Lancaster's Surgeon, Mr. Nadauld; in whom I was delighted to find an old friend of my father's, they having been students together at Hospital. He has a fine Cabbinn towards the after end of the ship, near the Officer's Quarters, and conducted me thither, very kindly giving me a glass of wine and asking me concerning myself and my father; expressing Great Sorrow to hear my father was dead. He then informs me that this His Present Post was but a stepping stone to Greater Things, and says that if I will be diligent and conscientious about my Duties, he will see that I am made a Full Surgeon at the end of the Year; which I took very kindly of him, for oft such as I have to wait a weary time before receiving Advancement. He did then pass to speaking of the ship, saying that the Lancaster though small and a sixth rater was a Gentleman's Vessel, all the officers being of Good Family; this to lead to my own affairs, he desiring that I should clothe myself more fitly; and I to acquaint him of the State of my Purse; on which he laughs, and says that he will arrange with the Commander that I receive an advance of Pay; which I thanked him heartily for. So to bed, once more sensible of the manner in which God is troubling over my affairs; so that this being finished I will to my knees to thank Him most Humbly and Deeply.

April 13.

An uproar this early morning. The man with the wife impressed at Blackstakes did sneak from his Hammock and attempt to get into a small boat secured at the stern; from which he was prevented by the Marine posted at the Alley leading to the Officer's Cabbinn; this man's musket going off in his grappling with the poor wight, so that the whole ship was aroused and the man secured and bound with strong ropes by the Watch. He was then thrust into the Bilboes until after breakfast; when Commander Hamilton and three other Officers sit in Judgement on him; finding him guilty of Attempted Desertion, so that he was sentenced to be flogged. But his circumstances being taken into account, and our Commander being a merciful man he was given only two dozen lashes. The crew and the Marines were summoned, and all arranging themselves as yesterday the man was roped with his arms above his head to the Mainmast, and then Ned Tollit lays on the lashes with a Tarred Rope with split ends; the wight proving sullen until the fourteenth stroke, when his Fortitude deserted him with a Loud Shriek; on which Mr. Nadauld steps forward and takes his pulse, and then nods to Commander Hamilton, who gives the signal to continue; and Ned lays on the rest, the man fainting at the twentieth blow; when a sailor hands Ned a bucket of water which he slings over him; and then he being semiconscious Ned gives him the rest as mere love taps; and the man was cut down and hurried below; and Mr. Nadauld comes over to me and says that I can attend him; which I do, going below to find the Flogged Man on his Stomach on the floor of the

Foc'sle, his mates all bent over him; and so to Minister to him, rubbing salt into the wounds and pouring a measure of rum down his throat, and so to get him into his Hammock; wondering I must confess whether such Treatment is like to make a good sailor of him; he being already so crazed that Whipping is like to turn him into a Savage Beast.

And so up on deck again, to find more Trouble; for a seaman due to return the night before had just come alongside Very Drunk in a wherryman's boat; and Commander Hamilton looks down at him, and then cries furiously to get him on deck; and then shouts to Ned Tollit, "Show me that Drunken Rascal's Backbone!" and so he was triced up to the Mainmast and Ned flogs him until his arm began to weaken; but though the sot had then received Thirty One Lashes and had passed from drunkenness to sobriety and so again to insensibility, still Commander Hamilton urged him to lay on, and did not cry "Cease!" until the man had received forty lashes more; by which time the flesh was most cut from his back; and then the Commander seeing that he could not be revived with sea-water as heretofore, orders him to be cut down, and he was, and carried below, this time, at my bidding, to the Cockpit; where on examination I found the bones of his ribs exposed in two places and so to dress the gashes, wondering whether he would recover; which I very much doubt, his Vital Spirits surely being shook badly with Drink and the Subsequent Punishment. And so to the deck once more, where I found Mr. Nadauld taking the air; and with him to the Captain's Great Cabbinn, where we found sundry officers gathered, amongst them Lieutenant Duhamel, they taking wine with Commander Hamilton, who enquires our business; and Mr. Nadauld to remind him that he had spoken to him about me; and so the Commander laughs, and stares at me, and says that I certainly look as though I need fresh Linen; at which Mr. Duhamel assents, remarking that I stank like an Ostler; at which all laugh, and then the Commander gives me a Paper to take to the Purser; and then as I took my leave, says that I have seen something of Navy Discipline that morning, and that the Fortitude with which the Rascals of Sailors learn to withstand flogging is the Reason why they are so Invincible in Battle; and more to the same effect; adding that he hoped for G-d's sake I was a good Chirurgeon, for he could not afford to lose any men, being already short handed; and so gives me leave to go ashore, and I to the purser to hand him my Paper and thereby received five pounds, this being two months advance pay, and which was a great relief to me.

I had to wait till after Dinner to get ashore, when the Gunner and Gunner's Mate took boat to the Ordnance Yard; and so I got ashore. Portsmouth is a town of medium size, like to be eclipsed by the

Neighbouring Suburb of Portsea, which is almost as big and still growing, many of the merchants having their houses there to be away from the streets of Portsmouth which is a Garrisoned Town and it's roads thereby crowded not only with Sailors but Soldiers, their conduct very often Most Reprehensible. The only building that interested me in Portsmouth was the fine stone fort newly built at the Southern end of the High Street. It is of course only fitting that a city whose history (I learn) dates from a founding by Richard the Lion Hearted King of England should be filled with the Appurtenances and Preparation for War, but I did grow tired of the Soldiers and the jostling of them, fights betwixt them and the Sailors being common; and so after equipping myself with a new pair of breeches, four shirts, two cravats, five pair of stockings, and a fine Naval Blue Coat–His Gracious Majesty King George having grown enamoured of a blue riding coat faced with white worn by the Duchess of Bedfordshire, and thereby desiring all holding posts in the Navy to change from Red Uniforms to Blue set with White–I did therefore take my parcels and repaired to a quiet Inn by the Waterfront, where I seated myself by the window having a fine view of the ships and the distant Isle of Wight; and there did take a stoup of wine and a small collation, marvelling at the merchantmen, which carry cattle and merchandise round from the Essex and Kent coasts and from Ireland, and at the black hulls of the Warships.

But Lord, I had been there but scarce a half-hour when I hear a great outcry in the street; and all those present did snatch up their hats and run out; and I was left, wondering at the awkward gait of a young Spark dressed as a Sailor, who had been seated with a Gallant a little older, also dressed as a Sailor, a little way from me. I to my feet, wondering what was to do, and then peering from the window see a Pressgang from our ship securing the Spark and the Gallant with him, and much noise thereby; the Spark screaming most amazing and the Gallant laying about him with his cane until one of the Sailors knocks it from his hand. And then our First Lieutenant Mr. Rose comes running, and the Gallant seizes him by his cravat; and the Lieutenant asks what is afoot; and one of the sailors knuckles his forehead and says they have catched two likely Recruits; at which the Gallant falls to swearing he is a Gentleman; and Mr. Rose with some heat pulls his neckcloth and replies that Gentry or no, he was taking him aboard; at which the Spark takes to screaming again; and the Lieutenant remarks that he has a Remarkable Shrill Voice; and one Sailor securing him with an Arm around his waist says with a Grin that he believes him to be no Man but a Woman; and the Spark breaks to blubbing and snatches off his Straw Hat; and Lord it was a Woman in truth, as a great mass of yellow curls comes rippling down to testify. Mr. Rose makes a bow to this Hermaphrodite, and begs her Humblest Pardon; and she falls to entreating him that he will let them both go, they being in Sailor's dress to go to a Masque to be held at some Lord's house the same afternoon; and the Lieutenant looks at her, being loath I could see to let the Gallant go, having taken a dislike to him; and one of the Sailors says with another grin that they being dressed as sailors they should surely secure one of them; and the Gallant bursts out cursing again, saying that they were both dressed as Sailors, and therefore it was as sensible to take either of them; to which the Seaman replied, staring at the wench's hair; "Aye, but Moll there d'ye see carries too much sail in her head-tops and top-gallants to be a good craft to cruise along with!" and the wench makes a set at him and tries to scratch his eyes out. So the Lieutenant at this display of temper bursts out laughing also, and noting the Firmness of the Lady's mouth, says to the Gallant, "Go your way! But shortly you will, tis plain, set out to sea as a Hen Pecked Frigate!" and so they left them, the wench reviling her protector that he did not forthright demand Redress from the Lieutenant; which one could scarce expect him in Sanity to do, Mr. Rose being taller by a good Head and Shoulders. Later when returned to the ship did see Mr. Rose returning with his men and four unlucky wights, one still holding a cook's wooden spoon, he having been at his Oven when they secured him. Tomorrow I learn we set forth with the Fleet on a cruise.

April 14.

This morning before breakfast I did repair to the Foc'sle to see how the men flogged yesterday did fare, the seamen I noted somewhat surprised at my visit. Found both of them in much pain, the Consumptive John Barlow ministering to them, he having picked up something of Physic and Surgery during his sojourn at the Infirmary. As both had some degree of Fever did bleed 'em both; the Drunk Man whose bones were exposed I do not think will live, he complaining of pains in his chest. And so to breakfast with the Under Officers in the Saloon, afterwards taking the air upon the deck, there to meet with Mr. Nadauld also walking, and he to enquire as to the two flogged men, and then straightway to ask me whether I did not think Commander Hamilton a very Agreeable and Condescending Man; to which I assented, having a mind to add that having met him but once I could not as yet have formed any opinion of him of Real Worth; but thought it imprudent to do so. And then the Officers came on deck, and after some little time our Captain; and much shouting, and blowing of Ned Tollit's whistle, and so to the tune of the Carpenter's fiddle the anchor was brought up, and the Tall Singing Sailor strikes up a new ditty, called, I believe, Drops Of Brandy, very appropriate for sailors.

Seaman: And why should I not love Johnny?
Chorus: And why should not Johnny love me?
Seaman: And why should I not love Johnny?
Chorus: As well as another bodie! etc.

Then the Commander bawled new orders, passed on by the Master, and the Fore Sheets were unfurled and the Sprit Sail unreefed, the Singing Sailor thereby striking up a new song, very jolly:

Seaman: We hove to our ships when the wind was sou'west, lads.
Chorus: We hove to our ships for to strike soundings clear.
Seaman: Then we filled our main tops'ls, and bore right away, boys,
Chorus: And right up the Channel our course we did steer!

and the men both on the Yards as well as the deck singing, the ship Rang with music, very enjoyable. The day was fine, and across the sunny waters we could hear the singing of the sailors of the other Ships of the Fleet; and I to think that despite its manifold hardships there was no life so fit for a Man as that of a Sailor's. Our Fleet did consist of the Commodore on board the Flagship the great Line of Battle ship the Ramillies; a frigate of thirty two guns; the Lancaster and another sixth-rater the

Mercury; and a sloop the Dragon; and as our sails were set the Commodore hoisted his Broad Pennant, and was saluted thereby by every ship in the Squadron with ten guns, he replying with the same. I did marvel at the System aboard the Lancaster and the Disciplined Bearing of All; as the Sails were unfurling Ned Tollit's whistle pealed again, and sixty sailors came running, six to each of the ten forward guns, the First Lieutenant Mr. Rose being in charge of these; the guns were run in, the charges rammed home, and then as the captains of each gun crew raised his arm, the gunner standing by the linstock flaming in his fist, the Commander gave an order, the Midshipman at the foot of the Poop ladder repeated it, the Linstocks were applied to the priming; and the sturdy ship rocked as the nine pounders went off with a Terrific Roar; I could see the shot skipping away across the sea, raising little plumes of Spray as they cut the Wave-tops. And then Commander Hamilton unfurled his colours, and the seamen struck up a Fresh Ditty and the look-outs were posted; and the Marines ran to the Waist and formed into line and beat their Drum; and we set out to sea, the Ramillies leading, the Frigate behind her and somewhat to the starboard Tack, the sloop being on her weather bow; and we and the Mercury almost in line, bringing up the rear; and so we stood down the channel, a seaman pointing out to me the white chalk of the Cliffs of the Isle of Wight, very pretty in the sunlight, and later those Crags which tooth the Southern Angle, these called the Needles, and very dangerous to Shipping when the Gales blow up the Channel; and I went below to see to my patients, Mr. Nadauld seemingly being Employ'd elsewhere, and to examine the ear of the Sailor, now progressing well, and another wight who had crack'd his thumb on a Spar, and one with a Constipation.

I did think our Squadron was bound for a cruise in the Channel and Northern coast of Spain; but meeting with Mr. Nadauld after dinner, he to inform me that Our Destination was not Fix'd, the Commodore expecting orders from London at the foot of the Channel. And sure enough, in the middle of the afternoon, our course being then East by East by South the Dorset coast on our lee the Ramillies heaves to and fires a gun; and then in an hour a brig comes up and lets go her anchor, and puts off a boat; and then those in her clamber aboard the flagship, as I did see through the spy-glass of Mr. Rose, he very kindly proffering it me; and then after a little while more we hear very faint the sound of distant cheers from the Ramillies, and those from the brig back to their boat and so to their ship; and the Commodore runs up a string of little flags, and fires another gun, and much excitement thereat on board our vessel; and I learn that we have received Orders to sail to the West Indie Isles, there to impress the Spaniards with a gesture of firm friendliness. And so Commander Hamilton gives orders that we should fire a salute of four shotted guns, and the other ships in the Squadron did likewise, and then we ceased from Tacking and set a course direct up the Channel, the Ramillies at first behind, but soon forging ahead with her Mighty Press of canvas. So tonight my cabin sways gently with the first of those Atlantic Billows that I learn from Ned Tollit do out away from Land rise to a Fury unbelievable.

II

April 15.

The winds continuing fair we did this day pass Land's End, it not visible for mist and the hour, which drew towards dusk. The flogged sailors improved; I do think that the one whose bones were bared will after all Make a Recovery; his back discharging very healthily, and not much Fever in his blood. The other wight's back also Goes Well but I do not like his Manner, it being sullen and morose; though I am glad to see that he does not extend this surliness to me. Barlow the erstwhile Consumptive has been aiding both these to their comfort, and with an eye to future Help I did this day discourse to him on the Rudiments of Surgery, he proving very Quick Witted thereat. After dinner I was summoned to the Commander's Cabbinn, and found him seated before a chart, Mr. Nadauld also there at another table throwing the dice with Mr. Duhamel, Mr. Butler, the first Marine Officer, and Mr. Lester the Second Marine Officer; and Commander Hamilton to enquire cheerily how the men went that had been flogged; and I to reply that they fared as well as might be expected; at which answer he frowned, and then enquired of me how long it would be before they were fit for duty; and I to reply at least a full week; and Mr. Duhamel looks up with a sneer and says, "A Week? You do not know your work, Master Sawbones! These are no lily-fingered damsels to be cosseted over; they are Rogues of Seamen who must be treated firmly, else they grow Insubordinate!" at the which I was about to answer him Angrily, only I did catch sight of Mr. Nadauld putting his finger to his lip and shaking his head at me. Commander Hamilton purses his mouth, and turning to Mr. Nadauld says that he must explain to me that this is not an Infirmary for the Convalescing of the Sick, but one of His Majesty's Ships, where a man must work or die; and so dismisses me, and I to walking on the deck in some Perplexity of mind, until Mr. Nadauld comes out and taking my arm says that I must remember now that I am a servant of His Majesty's and employed solely to preserve the health of the seamen so that the most work can be got out of them; the Humanities very well in their place, but not to be applied to common sailors, who were recruited from the Stews and naught but Gallows fruit; and so comes down with me to the Foc'sle, pinching his nostrils at the smell, and not examining the Seamen's backs at all, but standing off a little way plucking at his wig; and then on deck again says that they do very well, and that to give them longer to recover was to breed ideas above their Station in their Hearts; and so he to report to

Commander Hamilton, and I to seek the worthy Bosun Ned, and to inform him of all that had befallen and to ask him to find them some light work before the Lieutenants drove them to such place as the Spars where they would likely die; and he to get them with the Carpenter sewing Sail Cloth, so that he did report to Commander Hamilton that they were at work and all was Settled Peaceable. In the afternoon did pass much Sea-Wrack.

April 17.

These days we have stood out into the Atlantic, and very lonely and desolate the Ships do appear on its waste, they seeming but cockleshells, all but the Ramillies, that rides them with a stubborn English Pride. Much singing tonight from the seamen's quarters, they all gathered on the deck and chanting some sad Fare-Thee-Well songs; amongst those that did catch my Int'rest was one called "Polly M'Down."

April 18.

Still no ships seen but those of our Squadron. A school of Porpoise fish was off our bow today at noon, their Antics very quaint.

April 19.

Service on board taken by the Commander, the Chaplain being too sick to join the Lancaster.

April 20.

This morning it was found that last night we had lost touch with our Squadron, the day breaking to reveal not a soul in sight, and Commander Hamilton in a great Passion thereat, saying that the ship would be better manned by children and bumboat women than by his present crew; and so we sailed throughout that day, the lookout sighting a ship towards dusk, and giving a hail of "Sail-Ho!" and so we catch up with the Sloop of the Squadron, she having sprung a leak and signalling us to send her our Carpenter; so our Captain in a fury does so, and closes ship towards the Dragon; and we lay together until dawning, when the Pumps of the sloop having been made secure we separated, and set off once more towards our Destination; the Captain of the Dragon informing us that the Ramillies when last seen was bearing West by South, and likely not far ahead.

April 21.

This day a Marine slipped on the deck and dislocated his shoulder; so with Barlow's help to reduce it, the common seamen and the Musketeers being left to me to attend, Mr. Nadauld attending the officers. The Dragon still in sight, the wind fair.

April 22.

Sighted a brig at noon and gave chase, firing the forward guns to bring her to. She was naught but a

Portugee however with a cargo of small worth, so let her go. The Dragon on our weather bow, but yet no signs of the others. The backs of the flogged seamen now healing.

April 23.

Much excitement this day we sighting the tops of the Ramillies (we thought) but these turning out to belong to a French Forty Gun Cruiser; so that we did make signals to the Dragon and crammed on all sail, the Frenchman firing sundry guns at us, but she being slow—with weed Ned Tollit thought—we did by the mercy of God escape. Tonight the wind is getting up.

April 27.

Have been quite unable these last days to enter in this my Journal because of the tossing of the ship; there having arisen one of those terrible storms that make the life of the Sailor so Arduous. On April 24 the Wind blew with great force and sail was shortened and the Sprit sail Yard taken in; and then the Wind continuing and rising with even Greater Vehemence all sail was snugged, the guns secured, and we ran with bare Poles, the Captain saying gloomily that it would endanger us All to attempt to keep to the course pricked on the chart; and so we were swept far out, losing all sight of the Dragon; on whom and her crew may God have mercy she already being Leaky. Could scarce sleep on April 24 night because of the plunging of the ship, three times being thrown from my bunk. On the morning of the 25 going on deck for Air, that below decks being very Foul, did find the Wind had Whipp'd the Seas to a Hideous Fury, they crashing onto our decks from a height nigh as tall as our Masts, and so below again in haste, feeling not a little troubled in Mind. At noon the Great Yard of the Mainmast and its top were carried away and a most dismal crash like to Thunder thereat; and the Flogged Seamen with the Wife, who is I am Certain going Distracted, to scream aloud, "God have mercy on us all! We are going Down!" and so with Barlow's aid and two-three other sailors to secure him and bind him in his hammock, where I did bleed him to cool his Frenzy some forty ounces. And so we did Fly before the Wind and the seas all that day, none save the Watch venturing on deck, and the air growing very heavy below; and so all through the night, I endeav'ring to sleep but unable; being summoned at dawn by Ned Tollit to the Cockpit, where I did find two sailors Battered to Insensibility by the Waves, they having been swept against the Barge by a Heavy Sea. One man had the arm broken but not the bones protruding, and three great gashes across his Neck and Shoulder; the other in Graver Straits having had his Belly torn open by the Barge's broken timbers and his Bowels protruding through the wound. So to call Barlow and he holding the first sailor, and another wight a lantern, to wedge myself as best I might against the wall of the Cockpit against the Rolling of the Ship and to set the arm of the first sailor Fixing it with a charge of tow and tar; and then to attend the other man, doing him last as he was still insensible and like to die in any case; did sponge the protruding Bowel with sea water finding it to my relief mostly Mesentery and the man wearing only his britches at the time of his Accident and no cloth therefore in the wound; and pushed it back and sewed up the muscle and skin, this being at all times a Hazardous enterprise from the risk of plunging the needle into the Bowel and rendered a Thousand Times more so from the Intolerable antics of the Ship; I was as often on my side as on my feet. And so to sponge with sea-water and close up their sundry gashes, and to get them into their hammocks; bleeding both as a Discouragement of the Fever that will follow. And then to breakfast, being unable to shave for the tossing of my cabin; and the Seas still continuing high we did run before them all that day, and this morning a seaman was carried away by them, and no more seen. Today the wind and the sea both strong, though abating in Strength, and have ventured on deck. The hurt seamen do continue fair; I hope that the one with the Gashed Belly may live, his wound commencing to suppurate, but not unduly offensive. Did seek out Mr. Nadauld and held converse with him concerning the Flogged Seaman with the Wife; I convinced in my mind that he is going Mad, but Mr. Nadauld to laugh heartily, and say that whether he be so or no, he can still work, and must be kept working until he Grows Dangerous. No sail in sight; all on board do wonder of the Luck of the Dragon, she if not gone to the bottom, surely a Complete Wreck.

April 28.

A sail sighted to the North today, but passed without our gleaning anything as to her Country or Class. All the crew busy on decks repairing the rigging and the Carriages of the Guns, three of these being shattered beyond repair, and one of the Poop three-pounders gone overboard; and to rig a new Cap for the Mainmast. My two sailors feverish, but their wounds healthy. Did bleed each ten ounces and administered a Febrifuge; also threw up a Mercury Clyster on the Sailor with the wife, to distract the blood from his head to his entrails.

April 29.

Today sail was set and we got us back on our old course. At noon did sight the Frigate of our Squadron, and she to close under our Lee and to hail us asking what we had been at; and asked why we did not set the Main-tops and make more speed; and

Commander Hamilton to acquaint him of the Damage to our Mainmast, and the Frigate then bid us make all speed we could for land, the Ramillies being already far South with the Mercury making for Madeira. We were asked also what was become of the Dragon; to which our Captain made reply that she had not been since the 22nd; and so we separated, the Frigate taking note of the Latitude and Longitude where the sloop was last seen.

May 6.

These last days the weather, God being good, has continued fair, there being a Gale on the night of Sunday May 3 that cracked our Main Top again; but it was secured without further damage. Commander Hamilton very anxious to make all speed since the sea-water has leaked into the tubs of fresh water and these grow Rank. The seaman with the broke arm and the one with the Cut bowel to my great delight do progress well; was complimented by our Captain thereat. I take no pride to myself, however, since all these things are in the Hands of Our Almighty Father; as that Father of Modern Surgery the Frenchman Ambroise Paré did use to say, "I dressed their wounds, but God healed them." Do pray that we may shortly have some sun, the seamen's quarters are all steamy from the Walls being soaked with Water from the first Terrible Storm, and moreover Rank with the Bilge Washings; the same afflicts my cabbinn with sundry Grievous Odours. The pumps are manned daily, but our Timbers were much strained in the Storm so that she oozes water like a Basket.

May 8.

Today the last of the green provisions were served, these having been served out in small quantities only the past week. Most of the conies and hens were killed or drowned in the Storm, so that from now on us Common Men will feed on the Salted Meat. The animal Strength of these sailors does amaze me; the Flogged men, yea even the one whose bones were exposed now Quite Whole again, and out on the Yards; and the two damaged by the barge healing fast. I am struck by the manner in which the one with the Split Belly does mend; he was afflicted for some little time by a Grievous Catharsis, the which I took for a provision of Nature to ease the Congestion from his Bowel; this now ceased, though his motions still a little loose (I do mind me that they are kept so) and he quite easy in his mind; only normal pain in his belly which suppurates very nicely. Removed this day a splinter from the first finger of the Gunner's Mate Henry Jacobs, and he very grateful.

May 10.

Sunday, and a service on the deck, taken by Commander Hamilton and a Hymn very well sung reminding us of How Indeed we are in The Hollow of God's Hand.

May 11.

A great School of Fish to follow us today, and much Sea-Wrack; a sign Ned Tollit informs me that we approach Land.

May 12.

Yesterday did bend new canvas, and today sundry seamen to me suff'ring with a dryness of the skin the result of chafing of the Stiff Canvas Sails. Did what I could for 'em, drugs beginning to run short like every other commodity. Sighted an English merchant vessel bound for the Americas, and she to hail us for water, and we to give her what we could, though our own now scarce to be called Fresh. The sun appeared through the clouds, so that all have been enabled to take the Air. At my suggestion some sailors did bring up the man with the wounded Stomach, and right glad he was to be out of the dark noisome Foc'sle. The one with the broken arm tended him, both much enjoying "The Smell of Salt Water Again" and I to sit with them awhile talking, and did hear sundry Wond'rous Tales, of Mermaids and Fearful Portents and that Sea away on our Weather Bow which is a Graveyard of Vessels, being not so much Sea as a Stagnant Mass of Sea Weeds in which the ships are caught fast as in a Net. Certain it is that the Seas do hold many strange and mysterious Creatures. Did see today that Weird Conception of Nature the Shark, and those not on Watch to angle for it; not catching it, but taking besides many fish which were most welcome to add to our diet.

May 14.

Several of the seamen to me suffering with the Scurvy, their eyes puffy, and their gums sore and bleeding. They were not badly affected, but it is an Indication that we are needing Fresh Provision. Mindful of the teaching of Doctor Leeds did repair to the Galley and cozen from the Cook some celery and potatoes, he in some distress of mind lest it come to the ears of the Officers, particularly that worthy man Mr. Duhamel, who is cordially disliked by all; and so to feed my sailors, and to set them a-fishing; whereby words with the First Lieutenant, who demanded to know what they were all at; and I to explain to him, and he to say Sarcastik that "he supposed a Landsman would look upon a Ship as a Floating Cabbinn upon a River" and more to the same effect; only I catching a gleam in his eye did see that he was but Quizzing me; and so to converse with him as to our Object, he informing me that by Dead Reckoning we should sight Land within Two Days more.

May 15.

Much wind today, and Ned Tollit flung by the Antics of the Ship across the Wheel; at which much merriment.

May 17.

Sunday; at the service Commander Hamilton did pray very earnestly that the wind might abate and so we reach Harbour without more undue Toil. Sighted a Spanish Galleas in the middle of the afternoon, she alt'ring Course and Sheering off at sight of us, so that we let her go, it being Sunday.

May 18.

To distract the men's minds we did today have gun-drill and shooting off of the Cannon and much Row thereby; practise being needed as we pass into waters where Ships are often Enemies as Friends. Land approaching did to my cabbinn and write a letter to my Revered Uncle.

May 19.

Today sighted the Land, it lying West by South; by dusk the East Cape of Madeira was visible to our North some four leagues, and ev'ry one much cheered thereat; the Wights in the Tops and Lookout singing Out "Land Ho!" as though it might have been "El Dorado." My gentleman with the Split Belly so far Recovered that I can see a day or so ashore with all the Land's Gentle Gracious Gifts of Fruit and Warmth will put him on his legs again. Did examine the broken arm of the Sailor also and found a nice Callus; have no doubt that he too will mend to Usefulness after a few days on Land.

III

May 20.

A strange Bird did perch in our Rigging this day, being of the size of a Bantam Hen, but with a most strange beak and his feathers all glorious with green and blue and scarlet, so that he outdoes even the Officers of the Marines. Ned Tollit to inform me that such birds are the Common Fowl of the Forests of the Island; and I to marvel thereat. But a peep through Mr. Rose his spy-glass did show me that the slopes of this Great Island by which we sail are all covered with a thick Profusion of Vegetable Life such as I never thought possible; it is evident that in these Balmy Climes Nature is stirred to a Wanton Luxury. Mountains there be, their tops all clouded with mist, and deep ravines running down to the shore their depths tree-clad as in a Scots glen. Most all our crew were on deck today, hanging over the side to stare at the coast as though we were the Flying Dutchman returning to Port. My wounded very Cheery, and the one with the Split Belly to Essay a song; from which I stopped him, fearing lest he might break open his wound; and so the Carpenter's Mate did lend him a Stringed Instrument like a lute, on which he has strummed merrily all day.

May 21.

Was awoke this morning by a vast cheering and the firing of guns, and running on deck did find that we were entering Fonchal Roads, and a most Bewitching View of the town beyond, the white houses gleaming in the sunlight; the Ramillies and the Mercury there at anchor and we firing guns in salute, and they replying. And so below again to shave me and break my fast, and then on deck eagerly, to scan perhaps the most Perfect Panorama that my eyes may ever see; the road crowded with merchant ships and War vessels, there being a French frigate there as well as our own Line of Battle ships; and boats putting off from the Ramillies and from the shore, these last full of natives and fruit, the which our Seamen did eagerly buy, though none as yet allowed off ship till the Commodore had come aboard. His galley comes alongside, and he with an Officer to greet Commander Hamilton, and with him down to the Great Cabbinn to take wine; and I to learn thereby that the Ramillies and the Mercury had come to anchor there some two days previous, badly battered by the storm, which had made them turn South to this Island instead of Trying for the Azores. He comes on deck again and so away; and Commander Hamilton summons the men and says that as they will be there some days to await the return of the Frigate and the Dragon all would be allowed on shore; at which loud cheering. The barge was lowered, and those that could not crowd into it took boat in the native wherries about. I did first go below again to see my sick and to get the wounded up on deck and comfortable, and to see that they were provided with all necessities, buying them at their request some fruit, and to inform the One with the Wounded Belly that tomorrow I would see whether we might get him ashore for a little while; this resting upon the goodwill of our Commander, and he I realised too busy then to attend to such matters; being the relative of a Lord, and a galley from the Governor's House awaiting him.

And so to the Waist, where I found an Altercation very fierce going on; the Flogged Seaman with the Wife trying to get ashore in a wherry, but Lieutenant Duhamel of the Watch then on deck preventing him, saying that once he got ashore they would like never see him again; and the man very humble saying that surely he had earned a little Respite and Holiday; but Lieutenant Duhamel proving Obdurate he did grow sullen; at which I intervened, and to plead for the poor fellow; but Mr. Duhamel then grew furious, and seized the man by the arm and fell to cuffing him, swearing, and saying that he "was a Mutinous Rogue and Fit Gallows Fruit" at which the sailor straightens himself very sudden and gives Mr. Duhamel a most terrible blow in the mouth, and then leaps over the Bulwarks into the sea; and a great to do thereat, the seamen on deck running hither and thither, but none I did note making any Purposeful Effort to secure the sailor, who was then hauling himself on board a wherry bound for the shore. And so Commander Hamilton comes on deck, and falls to swearing, and desires a Marine to fire his musket; and I to attend Mr. Duhamel, who was crouched on the deck moaning his lips all split, and, Mr. Nadauld being already gone ashore with Mr. Rose and the Marine Officers, to call sundry sailors and to carry him to his cabin; nigh deafened by the roar of the Marine's musket, which went off close to my ear, but did see the ball went far from the wherry, and it then hid behind a Brig so that no more shots could be fired; and Commander Hamilton struck his cane with fury against the Poop railing, saying that he had never before been served by such a Slovenly, Incapable Crew; and so summons the Gunner and orders him to make a party and go hunt for the deserter; and so fuming down the side into the Governor's galley; and I to direct the sailors carrying Mr. Duhamel to get him into his cabbinn and so into his Bunk; where I did examine the wound, the Escaped Man having struck a Most Vehement and Ferocious Blow, that had dashed out three of the Lieutenant's Incisors and split the edge of his Lip for two inches; and so to close it with plaster, and administer a Purge of ten grains of Jalap, for the good of his gross body and for remembrance of his insolence, those aiding me seeming in no way cast down at this Mishap to their Officer but strangely cheerful. And so, having made Mr. Duhamel comfortable and bidding him rest where he was until the shock had abated and the Purge worked, did get me ashore in a wherry, marvelling anew at all the wonders spread out by the Hand of Nature so lavishly before my eyes and enjoying the Balmy Fragrant Breezes blowing from the land.

And how strange and Delightful it was to tread soil again and hear all round me the sibilant native tongue, a bastard mixture of Creole, Negro, and Spanish, so I am told; and to see the Bright Clothes of the Natives and the Strangest of Fruits in the Merchant Stalls. I did buy me some red-yellow globular fruits called Pineapples, and some yellow things in shape like a Bougie called Baniyanas, and did munch them in the roads and so up the Main Street and to view the Fine Mountains and the Fort on the Hill called the Pico fort. To stand on an eminence near this and view the Entrancing Panoramas was more than enough Reward for all the Perils and Hardships we had endured. I did roam for long amongst the groves of the trees, admiring the dusky olive skins of the natives, and the Beauty of the Young Maidens, these most catching, having eyes—and knowing how to use 'em, the saucy queans!—that would make the Fortune of a London belle.

So feeling hungry, I did repair again to the town, stopping oft to gaze Entranced at some new Gorgeous Flower or to harken to the Melodious Chirrup of certain little yellow birds called Canaries being about the size of the Common English Sparrow, and to a tavern where I dined, Realising to the Full why these Islands were called by Ancient Mariners the Blessed Isles of Peace. The Inn was thronged with Dons and French officers from the ships in the Harbour; also sundry merchants, Dutch, Portugee, Spanish and English; so that there was a Similar Clack of tongues to that heard at the Tower of Babel. On my way from thence I did pass an Alehouse from whence issued a jolly Chorus, and looking within spied the Gunner and his Search Party all Harmonious together; and they seeing me to hail me, and so I joined them; there being some other seamen from the ships of our Squadron there. The Gunner very quizzingly did ask after the Welfare of Mr. Duhamel, and I to ask him whether he and his men had found any trace of the Deserter, at which he laughs, and says that he has found no trace, adding that he bore the wight no ill-feeling since he had been the means of getting him and his Mates ashore when they were certain that they were surely doomed to stay and Watch the ship.

May 23.

Ordered off today for a cruise round the Archipeligo and to the Canaries, to seek for a Black Barquentine that has been annoying our Merchant Vessels by exacting heavy tolls.

May 24.

Sunday, and a Service on board very impressive amongst all these Monumental Memorials of God. Have been ashore each day past; yesterday got the sailor with the Wounded Belly ashore, his wound quite closed, but I anxious lest his bowels break out again, the skin still soft.

May 25.

After breakfast did walk on deck and espy a brig passing, that did seem familiar to me. So to obtain a Telescope and to peer at her; when I recognised her for that ship that had Int'rupted the Aim of the Marine the day the Man with the Wife deserted; of whom no trace has since been found, and Commander Hamilton much put out thereat. The brig was all busy with men making Sail, she setting a course for Portugal; and I to espy that one man was the Spit of that Escaped. Mr. Rose did join me and taking the glass from me peered at the ship long and earnest; then putting it down, turns to me with a little smile and nods; and as I stared at him, says very soft, "Blessed are the Merciful!" and so goes to about His Duties; and I to take another squint, and see that it was indeed the Man, and that he must have slipped on board the brig when his wherry was hidden that moment behind it. So to my own duties, somewhat thankful that the Wight was once more bound for his home and his Wife. We took on board at Fonchal puncheons of Fresh Water and several casks of Fruit, so it is to be hoped that the Scurvy may abate.

May 27.

This day a Grievous Calamity. Passing a Rocky Isle not marked on the Chart the Mercury our Consort did run aground with such force that her Mainmast tumbled down with the shock; and five seamen and two Marines killed. We did stand by until She was Got off, but she was then in such Parlous condition that she returned to Harbour, her Pumps full at work as she has started her forward timbers. This does seem to be a most unlucky voyage; the Dragon I fear has been lost with all aboard, and the Frigate not returned when we left, thus the Ramillies stopped in harbour to await her; and now the Mercury crippled, and we already far off our course to the Indies because of that Vile Storm; though I learn that in such instances as these, where a Fleet has to venture into the Great Sea Wastes, a margin of some months is always allowed each way.

May 29.

These days we have beaten about the Seas the wind being contrary. The sailors and the marines much improved by their Holiday ashore so that there is little for me to do. Lieutenant Duhamel is out and about his duties again, weakened by the Dosing Purge I gave him and by an Abscess which came up on his mouth the result of a fragment of broken tooth being driven into the lip; the which Mr. Nadauld lanced, and which was the saving of me, for I had thereby an excuse for purging him, Mr. Nadauld being somewhat annoyed thereat. Have passed my days in fishing, there being many strange Insects in these Warm Waters.

May 31.

Sunday and a day of rest. The wind dropping completely, there was little to do, and all basked on deck. I wrote to my Aunt and Uncle.

May 31.

Today, the Isle of Bugio lying astern some five leagues, we did sight a schooner to whose Aspect Commander Hamilton took exception, and so we did give chace, firing our bow carronades. But the schooner proving nimble Fled Away like a Sea Hind due South, and so we made full sail after her. To-night we are still in pursuit, and it is believed that we shall overtake her by dawn if we do not lose her in the murk. There has been much excitement aboard with polishing of guns and sharpening of cutlasses, it being thought likely that she is the Consort of that vessel we seek; or perhaps She Herself.

June 1.

Much exasperation and hard swearing today by all, the Master having kept a course during the night after a riding light that dawn reveals as naught but that of a Dirty Spanish coaster, and our Schooner nowhere to be seen. We did close in on the Spaniard, but she proved to have naught on board save some hides and goats; and so we did appropriate several goats for fresh meat and their milk, and let her go, her Captain swearing and weeping something to marvel at.

June 4.

Today did sight the Island of Lanzarote, and hailed an English merchantman for news; but naught of interest. Did catch a shark, and two seamen to aid me pull it aboard; Ned Tollit informing me that it's backbone would make a Fine Cane if properly prepared did hack it out, the old cook taking the rest of the body to serve to the men.

June 7.

Sunday, and service interrupted by a cry from the Look-out of "Sail Ho!" and course altered to bear down on the ship; which as we approached we did see was naught but a scuttled Wreck of a French barque, her masts down and trailing alongside, all her rigging gone, and her sides blackened with fire and smeared red with blood; so we closed in on her, and receiving no Answer to our Hail a boat did put off under Mr. Rose and so to board her; and he and his men to tramp about, and call to us that there "Were Naught but Dead Men aboard!" and then going below we did hear other shouts, and then he appears, struggling with a Mad Woman, and his sailors carrying two other seamen all bloody. And so they put back to us, and our men crowd the rail on that side as they come aboard; and Commander Hamilton comes down to the Gangway to meet 'em. The Woman young, not ill-favoured, but quite Crazed; and so she was handed to Mr. Nadauld for treatment. The other two Wights greatly gashed but still breathing, and so they were brought to the Cockpit, and I to revive them, though I did see that they were Almost Sped.

And so after a little Commander Hamilton comes down to me, and asks me whether they have spoke yet; it proving impossible to get any Reason from the Woman, she being all Abroad from Having been Forced; and I did reply that I did not think either man would ever speak again in this Life, they already being As near Dead as makes No Odds; in illustration of which one man whose head I was holding gives a Sigh and Straightens his Limbs, and so dies; but under the Influence of Spirits the other revived somewhat saying in broken whispers in French that a Black Barquentine had overtaken them that morning as the Night gave Way to Day, creeping up under cover of the murk and so suddenly laying them aboard; men pouring off her on to the Frenchman so that half the crew were butchered before they knew what was afoot; the poor man speaking and two others getting to a brass carronade and loosing it off so that the Barque caught Fire slightly; but they were overpowered and cut down, and the Bloody Rogues who had attacked them then swarmed throughout their vessel, seizing all of value that they possessed and making Sport with the Captain's wife; and so to cut down the rigging and hack the ship about as though they were Madmen; and so to leave as sudden as they had come; and no Frenchman on his feet, but the most part dead; and those that lived so badly hurt that they died shortly from their wounds. He being then exhausted through having fought so long for his Life, Commander Hamilton did make sign to me, and so left me; and I to get the poor fellow into a hammock; he Horribly Torn with a sword thrust through his chest and two gashes across his head, one of which has Penetrated I fear me through the bone to the brain beneath. Did dress his wounds, and bleed him, and so to the deck again, where I found a prize crew putting off to the Frenchman in charge of the Quartermaster and the Senior Midshipman. We did then send aboard Sundries such as Sailcloth and Ropes, the Carpenter's Mate having gone with the Prize Crew to mend the Masts, and then we set off away from them, Commander Hamilton very vehement to catch these Pirates, and hopeful that they be not far off; and so we have sailed throughout this day, coasting along to Keep a Sharp Eye on the Ravines and Creeks of the Island; I ministering to the wounded man, he sinking fast so that I doubt me that he will last the night. The body of his Companion has been taken back to the Frenchman, our Commander having a Fancy that he should be given Sea-Burial from the decks of the vessel he had so well defended.

June 9.

Have been too Fatigued these last days to write in this my Journal, having had much to do and an experience which I suppose I shall in time grow used to, but which at this first onset has Wearied me beyond belief. On the morning of the Eighth the French seaman died; and we committed him to the Deep with Full Rites, the Musketeers firing a salute as his canvas wrapped body was slid into the sea. Then at noon we did espy the masts of a fair-sized ship standing up from behind the trees of a creek; but before we could sail opposite to that point we did see the masts move, and a ship sailed out in front of us and stood out to sea. She was a three-master not like either that Schooner we had chased nor that vessel that the French sailor had described: but as she yawed to the breeze, all did see that her starboard beam was streaked with fire blackening, partly obscured by paint or tar; at which a great Roar went up from our sailors, who shook their fists at the craft very vehement, one wag getting up in the Bowsprit Yards and calling to the Vessel to let only him aboard and he would show them that they could not take liberties murdering poor Froggies and Raping their Women; and the Ship fires a swivel-gun at us in derision and so sweeps off to the South-South-East, showing a very pretty turn of speed; and I to learn from the talk about me that she was a big ship probably carrying heavy metal, that disguised herself by raising or lowering her bulwarks; and so to watch her forging ahead, we peppering her with our forward pieces. She did attempt to strike straight out to the Open Roads, but this move our Commander did thwart, hemming her in along the coast where the hills cut off the Wind and so slowed her; we being further out had of course the Benefit of the Full Breeze.

Thus we ran, pursuer and pursued, for nigh three hours; and then as we sat at meat there came a Mighty Shout of Jubilation and the crash of our forrard nine-pounders; and so running on deck in

A Naval Engagement of the British Fleet

(AFTER A STEEL ENGRAVING)

much excitement, my mouth All Dry, I saw that we had approached a Headland and that the Pirate in swinging to weather this had lost the wind completely, and was now Going About Tacking, revealing her broadside to us so that the two forward nine pounders on the Starboard bow had been loosed from their tackle and brought to bear on her; and so we closed in on her, Commander Hamilton noting careful our Foes mishap and standing out to sea. Thus as I hung to the Ladder Rail, we closed in, and even as the Foe caught the wind and set off again, we came about with a suddenness that threw me from my feet and gave her a Broadside of our Heavy Ordnance, so that I surely thought the Pirate was sunk. But before the smoke cleared away there was an answering roar, and shot came whistling aboard and a marine near me was flung against the barge all pulped and smashed. I ran to aid him but he was dead; the ribs were standing out from his white cross-belt. Shot were now flying free and I thought me I should be in my cock-pit, and so I ran forward, crouching low I will confess for fear of the missiles that hummed across the deck. There were three more dead men on the deck, seamen from the forward ordnance; one only I found still breathing, but as his head was all smashed in it was of no avail for me to drag him below. I could see that the Cockpit would be full enough ere long.

Clamb'ring down the ladder I saw a Disturbing

sight; through the smoke rifts I catched sight of the Pirate ship's side, and where there had been smooth black timbers there was now grinning a row of open gun ports presenting artillery as numerous as our own. There was another Outcry from our men, this time of Fury; a sinister black Flag was creeping up the mast of our Adversary; she had broke her Lousy Ensign of a white scull and crossbones on a black sheet, that they call the Jolly Roger; and as I hesitated a wild shriek from above me, and a poor devil of a Midshipman tumbles out of the Foretop and plumps on the deck beside me; and I hear all his bones break, and drop to aid him, but the Great Artery of his Left Thigh burst and spouting like a fountain so that I saw he would soon be dead; but to snatch off my kerchief and bind it round as a Ligature; and then passing my hands over him did find that the Parietal Bone of His Scull on that same side was all loose beneath the skin; and so to beckon to a passing seaman and to roll him into the scuppers, where he might die in peace. And so down the ladder and into the Cockpit, where I found Mr. Nadauld sawing off the arm of a Marine, Barlow the erstwhile consumptive standing by and aiding him; for in Battle all men are equal, and Officer and common seaman, Midshipman and Marine, all are brought to the Cockpit for attention and no distinction is made between them. The Cockpit already hazy with Gun Smoke and the Great Lantern lit;

although it was broad noon above, it was necessary to close all but the Alley from the Foc'sle since there was a risk of Spars and Rigging and Cannon Shot tumbling into the Cockpit and embarrassing the Humane Work of the Surgeons; thus it was as dusk in that quarter, a dusk only Emphasised by the Lantern and the Glow of the Brazier where the Surgical Irons were heating; and this perhaps as well, for those not Accustomed to Chirurgery might grow Appalled at the Sights. I to aid Mr. Nadauld and to find that he was a Clever Surgeon enough; the arm on the floor almost before the seaman had recovered his Wits from the blow that had smashed his Appendage; there being no time for niceties of Ligaturing Vessels, a hot iron steeped in Tar was clapped to the Stump, and the Flaps secured over with a binding of tow.

The fight now growing Hot, as we did hear from the Prodigious Row on deck; the roof of the Cockpit resounding to the thump of tumbling spars and cannon-shot and the whole place rocking to the discharge of our guns; and those on deck shouting and bawling half-demented; and the Midshipmen screaming to repeat the orders; and wood work cracking and rigging parting with a noise like a score of fiddles; Lord, such a din as my pen cannot describe, and which blended with the shrieks and groans and lamentations in the Cockpit might well have been taken for a Court in Dante his Inferno. The seamen were now continuously carrying down wounded men; some with their heads all broken; some with limbs shattered with cannon balls; others with their bodies penetrated by slivers of wound and metal gouged off the bulwarks and guns; others all mashed from the falling Spars; so that speedily the space was filled, and Mr. Nadauld shouts for those treated to be carried out into the Alley; and still they were carried down, until my arm grew wearied and numbed from cutting and my fingers cramped about my instruments; and the room ran with blood and brains, and Mr. Nadauld soaked thereat till he looked more like a butcher than the man I knew and I in no better case. Not once did the Aweful Noise above abate, and I reckoned that we were being hard pressed, these Pirate ships carrying I have heard a full press of men; and then suddenly even above the Row there rises a Great Cheer from our seamen, and I feel the ship move beneath my feet, and hear the voice of our Commander very faint "Stand by to Board Ship!" and then a pause and then a Grinding Shock that hurled me off my feet so that I fell with my hand across the face of a dying Marine; and his teeth snapped at me.

And so I to my feet again and to see Mr. Nadauld snatch off wig and coat and hurl them out into the Alley and he to shout at me "What was I staring about me like a Fool for?" and to help him remove the thigh from the Gunner's Mate then just brought in, to give him a blanket three times folded to bite on and then to wedge him against an angle of the wall with my body so that his struggles might not unduly embarrass my superior; did then push back the bowels of a Marine and stitch the flesh over them, knowing full well that he would die, for his uniform had been carried into his entrails and we had to pull them out all bloody; and to drag a sliver of bronze shot from the head of a gunner and he dying thereat to roll him out of the way; and then the press of wounded diminishing somewhat did to the door, feeling Mighty Sick from the Vehemence of my Efforts and Emotions, there to look up through the ladder Hatch at the sky, all barred and crossed with Tumbled Riggings and Spars and a musket and the body of a Marine whose corpse dripped blood slowly into the Alley; and to glance round me for water, and then one Powder Boy looks up from ministering to the gunner and gives me to drink from a bucket; and Mr. Nadauld to scream at me again in fury for A Lubberly Lout who thought this was a Holiday; and so back again into the murky gloom of the Cockpit, and to aid him once more, this time with the Second Officer of Marine, whose ancle had been shattered with a musket ball. The din still continued, though the Thunder of Artillery had died away to a few scattered shots, being replaced with a crackling of pistols and muskets and the clashing of steel on steel, and a wild shrieking and hurrahing, so that I did realise that we were boarding the Pirate, but no time for thought thereby, for a fresh lot of wounded were now trickling down, many supporting themselves, being gashed with cutlasses and not stunned by being struck with Cannon Shot; so that we had more work still and did not get on deck for Air till above two hours had passed from the time of our First Broadside.

Then, all the wounded being attended to save those with scratches, whom we did attend in the evening or the following morning, and the living got into their hammocks and the dead laid out in rows ready for burial, needing only the Carpenter to sew their Sail-cloth Shrouds round them, Mr. Nadauld did call his voice very, very hoarse for men to wash out the Cockpit and remove the evidences of our work; these being collected five buckets full and being slung overboard; and then he did with me to the Decks above, and mighty glad I was to feel the sea-breezes on my poll and breathe fresh air after the Mephitick Stenches below. The Ship looked then as though she had been in the Grip of a Tornado; her Mizzen split, three Great Yards and the Sprit of the Foremast shattered and lying on the decks; the bulwarks all holed and splintered, and the rail in places gone altogether; cannon displaced, their trucks broke all to pieces; and rigging trailing every where, so that one had to be careful where one trod lest one caught one's foot and tumbled down, the decks being all greasy with blood and the water the gunners had thrown from time to time over the pieces.

The Pirate ship lay along side, in no better state; her men lying in heaps, there being no surgeon aboard her; but for the most part dead, for even those with broke limbs had endeavoured to prevent the progress of our men, so that they had been stamped down into the decks; some I did attend however, Mr. Nadauld saying that he had no Int'rest in such Scum, and going to his cabbinn to bath and change his clothes, also to comb out a new wig, the one he threw away being spoilt beyond hope of repair. Our men have secured only eight Pirates, many throwing themselves into the sea rather than surrender, in the manner of the old Romans; though one must not carry the Comparison further, these Pirates being in Truth the foulest visaged of Galley Rats. And so being almost beside myself with all that I had that day seen and heard I did follow Mr. Nadauld's example and to bathe in a bucket of sea-water, and changed my clothes; then to sup, the officers very jubilant at our victory; and so to bed, so weary that even the stench from just beyond my door and the moans and cries of the sufferers in the seamen's quarters a little further forrard could not keep my eyes from closing. Today we have been mending ship and committing the dead to the seas;

this a most doleful business, for we have lost heavily in this brisk encounter, to wit:

Two Midshipmen.

The Quartermaster.

The Third Marine Officer.

The Master's Mate; he posted as the custom is at the fore-topsail braces, and carried away overboard by a cannon shot to be no more seen.

Eight Marines.

One Gunner.

Eleven Seamen.

And there are some yet to be added to this Account, for some of the wounded are mortally hurt; for example the Marine out of whose belly I pulled his coat. The wounded comprise:

The First Lieutenant Mr. Rose, a pike thrust in the chest, he being one of the first to jump upon the Pirate's deck.

The Second Officer of Marines, a musket ball in the ancle.

A Midshipman with a cracked scull from a tumbling spar.

Two of the Carpenter's crew, struck by ditto.

Nineteen Seamen, with sundry wounds; four at least I do not think will recover.

Eleven Marines, three of whom are dying now.

These are the serious wounded. Three other Marines are slightly wounded with scratches about the hands and face and seven seamen likewise; also a rascal of a Powder Boy who bobbed up on deck when we boarded the pirate and received as admonishment a rap on the sconce from the Officer of Marines. Was mighty busy all yesterday attending to the wounded, those whose limbs have been removed, fifteen in all, four having lost only sundry of their fingers and toes and one hapless wight an ear, being in much Fever and Distress from their Economies recoiling after the excitement of the fight. All hands very busy repairing ship and mending rigging, and a prize crew being placed in command of the Pirate; much cheer at finding the Hold of the Robber full of rich merchandise chests of bullion, church ornaments, and also some crates of fruit, grapes, oranges, and potatoes, these almost as valuable and enough for all so the wounded seamen did greatly benefit. As we have now two prizes, and our aim in seeking out and destroying the pirate is accomplished, we have gone about and are making sail once more for Madeira with intent to rejoin our Fleet.

IV

June 10.

One of the Marines died early this morning, and after dinner another, a sailor. The Marine whose belly was ripped sunk into a stupor; he will I fear me shortly die. Am perplexed with that sailor whose ear I removed; there is vastly more discharge than is healthy, and it would seem that the Temporal Bone of that side is injured; the man complaining of an intolerable headache and very feverish. To bleed and purge him, and to dress the wound anew. The scars of the wounded commencing to grow foul did take Mr. Nadauld aside, and at his suggestion did cause all to be brought out and laid on the floor of the Forrard Between Deck, where they can receive the fresh sea-breezes. Went aboard the Frenchman in the afternoon to search for drugs, ours being almost exhausted, and did find a few simples, though naught of great value. Mr. Nadauld informs me that Mr. Rose fares well, but that he likes not the look of the ancle of the Second Officer of Marines there being much discharge and swelling, so that he fears that he will have to remove the foot.

June 11.

A woeful sight this morning on stepping into the Alley. Another Marine dead during the night, also two seamen both having lost their right legs, one at the knee, the other at the hip. So to remove them, and being made dismally aware of my shortcomings by these their deaths, to attend the others, in something like a fury of mingled fear and exasperation. Oh, God, if we only had more drugs! Of what avail is it to be dubbed Surgeon and to be looked up to for help when one's hands are tied and skill rendered empty through having naught but one's fingers to aid one! Did bleed all the wounded, and to dress their wounds with sea-water and tar, these being the only Physick I had, and so to make all as comfortable as I might; cheering the downcast, and feeling a most Hypocritical Rogue thereby; and so to send a Powder boy in search of a certain member of the Carpenter's crew, and he coming to set him to play cheery jigs on his fiddle to the poor sick, that their Minds be distracted from their Dolour. Then to breakfast, and after with Barlow the once-consumptive to the Hold, and there did milk one of the goats and Barlow bearing two pails of milk and I with my arms full of fresh meat and fruit to my Patients, each and all muttering Thanks, catching of my hand, and calling on God to bless me; and so I have continued throughout this day, watching over them and ministering to them. Commander

Hamilton did visit us at noon, and to speak kindly to me, praising all that I did; and Mr. Nadauld summoning me after dinner to the cabbinn of the Marine Officer, where after some discussion, he pleading very heartily not to be rendered a cripple, we did Resolve Not to Amputate the Foot; and so to lance the swelling at the end of his shin, there running forth a great quantity of blood-streaked pus, so that he should have much relief and indeed says that he is more comfortable. We inserted a tent in the wound; bled him ten ounces and threw up a clyster, not wishing to Aggravate his Stomach by giving a Laxative by the mouth. Then to view Mr. Rose, the Pike having passed through the Great Breast Muscle Pectoralis and so reflected by a rib beneath to pass beneath the Axilla ploughing the Serratum Superius Muscle and has likely touched the Intercostals, since the gash is deep. Mr. Nadauld has cunningly closed the whole with plaster, leaving a tent inserted at its lowest extremity that the pus may run forth and so not hinder the growth of The Scar. Bled him, and administered a Laxative five grains of Jalap; he will do well. The Marine with the torn belly still sunk in a stupor, his pulse now very weak and soft; blistered his stomach, bled him and threw up a clyster; his death though is surely only a matter of hours; am grateful to God that he is Sunk in a Stupor, for the Agony from the Injury would be very great, the Guts surely are Torn.

The weather continues temperate and cool, for which I am duly grateful; the wind, though fitful, has blown mostly from East by South by East again so that we make good progress.

June 12.

Committed to the deep today the body of the Marine mentioned last in yesterday's record, I being summoned from my cabin an hour before breakfast to find him stiff and cold. One of the Bloody Rogues of Pirates has died also, being wounded in many places about the head from being struck down at the first boarding of our men and so trampled into the scuppers. My other patients do well; still much discharge from the head of the seaman from whom I removed the Ear. Blistered his poll accordingly. More discharge also from the ancle of the Marine Officer; tonight a piece of wadding has come forth from the wound, at which Mr. Nadauld very jubilant; we had removed the bullet and subsequent probing revealed naught that we could suspect as abnormal; but now friendly Nature has Intervened to remove with Subtly that which Man's Poor Art might not do. Sent aboard two Puncheons of Water to the French prize her Water Casks being somewhat foul with green life. Passed and hailed a Brig out of Bristol, her sailors crowding the Ratlines to cheer us.

June 14.

Sunday, and a most Grateful Service to God in which all did join, to give Thanks for our Victory. A shred of bone came away from the scull of the seaman whose ear was removed; wonder whether this is due to the Importunities of my Blisters; trust that now he will mend without further ado. The stumps of those seamen with Amputated Limbs and Digits progressing, plenty of healthy discharge and no undue inflammation. Their quarters grow somewhat foul; did prevail on Ned Tollit to move them to fresh Palliasses and wash down the decks; though the odour still lingers somewhat.

An Island sighted today that I am informed is one of a small group lying Northward of Bugio, which we have not yet sighted; so it is thought that we have passed Bugio, and thus are making good progress; our speed delay'd by our Prizes, whose Jury Masts cannot take a great press of canvas. Today the wind has dropped so that all three of us have been becalmed; and the weather sultry did with Commander Hamilton's permission get those fit to be moved on deck, whereby they were greatly cheered; their comrades singing sea-chanties and Yarning to them. It is interesting to note how the wounds inflicted during such an action as ours fall into a Number of Categories; namely, those hit by Cannon Shot, usually on the head or legs, and thereby either killed instant, smashed to a pulp; or grievous hurt with great breaking of bones and bruising of flesh; those struck by Musket Balls, usually in the head or body, from the Aimed Fire of men in the Tops or standing in the boats; those receiving balls in the head or body from musket fire in the Tops usually dead or mortally hurt, since the Angle of Aim ensures that the ball strike downward through the body thereby injuring the Vital Centres; especially does this apply to those wounded thus in the head; I did see three men where the missile had struck the crown and so passed through the Brain to find exit through the body or neck, in one case near the base of the Vertebral Column; those wounded from Fire from the Bulwarks or Boats being luckier, since the ball frequently passed clean through the shoulder or neck. Thus the Officer of Marines was saved, he climbing into the barge to take the place of the Third Marine Officer who was posted there as the custom is with eight Musketeers; being struck down as I have detailed by a shot from a Pirate in the Main-top which passed through his hat to emerge from his spine low down in the Back; the Pirate being brought down by a shot from one of the Marines there posted, but the villain not being killed did take aim again as he lay in the Scuppers with a pistol whose ball struck the Second officer in his ancle. Then there are those injured in the hand-to-hand fighting; receiving either pike or sword thrusts in the body or neck, or cutlass gashes across the arms, face, or legs. There were of course injured that were not hurt in any of these ways; for instance one Pirate broke his leg through slipping on the deck; but the Major portion of my patients have been wounded in the Divers Manners detailed and their Injuries are serious in the same order; all save one of those whose limbs or digits were Amputated were struck by Cannon Shot; the exception being a Marine whose foot was crushed by the tumbling down of one of the Fore-Jeer Blocks. Today shoals of tiny fish swam past the ship.

Passing a Craggy Island called the Sail Rock did see through a spy-glass seals basking on the shore, a great multitude of them, with many young cubs. The Great Mountain of Madeira sighted this evening.

June 15.

Off Fonchal Bay this morning, and did meet a French Cruiser of Forty Guns putting out; and she to hail us, asking whether that prize the merchant ship was the Marie Therèse; and on learning that it was, did heave to, and send off a boat, and her captain comes aboard to ask whether any of her crew alive; and Commander Hamilton to reply, No, not one, save the wife of the Captain; and the Frenchman to ask whether he might have care of her; and our Commander to say that he might, most certainly, the wench being now recovered, and Distracting all His Officers with her incessant chatter, she not being able to speak any English; and so the French Captain, finding us friendly, to say that he should take possession also of the Merchantman the Marie Therèse, she being a French boat; at which Commander Hamilton grew enraged, saying that he had shed good blood for her and would in no way relinquish her; telling the Captain that he should keep better Watch and Guard over those ships sailing under his flag; and the Frenchman thereby to grow enraged also, and pointing to his Frigate says that he has twice as many guns as us, and would blow us out of the water; at which Commander Hamilton roars at him for an Impudent Sprig of a Dancing Master, saying that it was not guns but the men that served 'em that won battles; and adding that the first musket shot would bring down the English Squadron to which he belonged; pointing to the Ramillies lying at anchor in the Harbour; so that the Mounseer turns on his heel and goes back to his ship with the Woman, and we follow our two prizes into Port; Commander Hamilton having flagged 'em, as soon as he clapped eyes on the Frenchman, to make all sail to get into Port under the guns of our ships. And so we into Harbour, and a salute from the Ramillies, and I to attend my sick, all doing well, and cheered at the thought of Land and rest from the Tumbling of the Ship. The Admiral comes aboard, and talks with our Officers, and to compliment them; and walks about the decks to see the Damage; and even descends to speak cheerily to the wounded; which I thought kindly of him. Then he goes off again with Commander Hamilton to inspect the Prizes; which are to be offered at Auction to the Merchants in the Harbour and the Authorities; it being thought that these last might wish to make a Gun-boat of the Pirate Ship, she being sound and speedy. At noon a File of Soldiers came aboard from the Fort to remove the Prisoners; it is likely that they will be dealt with summarily, the Dons being very merciless towards such Rogues. Our boat being surrounded by many wherries carrying natives with their produce, sundry of these have been allowed on ship, and have only recently left; towards the dusk some producing their Guitars our Commander did permit them to sing to us; so that we have had a Little Concert; very enjoyable amongst the Balmy Airs blowing off the land. The wounded do well, though there is still much Inflammation about the site where I removed the Ear of that seaman concerned; do fear me that though the wound will scab and form Cicatrix, his brain may be affected always; there must surely be Inflammation proceeding within as without. The Ancle of the Marine Officer still discharging; the Tent has proved its use, allowing the escape of much Vile Turbidities.

But Mr. Nadauld does not consider (and I agree with him) that any Joint Oil or Synovia is flowing out; thus it would appear that the ligaments are not ruptured so that though he will have a stiff Foot to the End of his Days, he will be able to walk, though with Stiffness; and this of course will abate with the years, as the Muscular Action breaks down the Adhesions.

June 16.

An English merchantman sailing tomorrow for home, the Admiral has desired it to take the crippled wounded; so today we have been busy slinging those with Amputated Limbs into the barge and so conducting them to their New Home. The Master of the Vessel a worthy man, and to have moved part of his cargo to make 'em a Sick Bay; there will be also as passenger a Surgeon named Mr. Bliss, returning to England to Rehabilitate Himself after being near to Death with the Fever the sailors call Yellow Fever; so that all the wounded will be properly cared for. I did have converse with Mr. Bliss, and found him a kindly and clever man, Enthusiastic about his work; he will return either here or to the Indies as soon as he has regained his Strength, so that it is Possible I may meet him again at a future date. Our wounded Officers are to stay aboard, they having naught that will keep them from Duty when recov'red; and the English ship has given us six of her men, and eight have been sent from the other ships of our Fleet; so that we shall not be unduly short-handed. Getting the wounded slung took me all through the day so that I got no Dinner; this late afternoon I have been ashore with Mr. Nadauld to get fresh supplies of drugs and the like from the Apothecaries; he has also bought himself a Fine New Wig to replace that one spoilt in the Action, and I also in the same shop bought me two new shirts, a kerchief, and a pair of Cord Breeches hoping that these will stand the Sea-Air better than my cloth ones, which have all rotted; so that even the Carpenter, a tolerable fine tailor, now despairs of them, saying that there is no room for new patches.

June 17.

The English merchantman sailed at noon today, I then bleeding a Marine with a gashed arm, he having some degree of fever; and so finishing did run up on deck, to find it crowded, all the seamen clust'ring at the bulwarks to watch the ship run up her Sails and forge into the Wind; our Carpenter seating himself on the Capstan and striking up very slow and solemn:

Oh, sailor, where are ye bound for, away across the seas?

which song the Tall Singing Sailor did take up, and his comrades all joined in the refrain:

To the Islands of the Blest
Where no storms will me molest.

So that amongst all the cheering and halloo-ing many were silent and there were some wet cheeks; for amongst the wounded hobbling to the rail of the merchantman were many friends and relatives of our men, whom they might never see again; moreover, those on our ship were sorrowful at the parting of the wounded; for though they had scant comfort on ship, yet at home, even when recovered from their injuries, there was little but misery and starvation awaiting them; people ever making much of Hearty Folk, but leaving the Helpless and Infirm to Rot in the Gutter. I did see one sailor of ours whose brother was aboard the merchantman climb into the Ratlines and Hail his brother, "Carry my best respects to Mother, Jim! Tell her I will be back in Two Years with my pockets full of Gold for all of us!" and did see the man to whom he spoke lifted up by two seamen of the merchantship, he having lost his leg at the knee in the Action. And so the ship put out to sea; and I to my sundry duties, trusting that the Merciful Father of All would have them in safe keeping.

June 19.

The seven Pirate Rogues executed this morning, being summarily condemned in Toto by a Special Court; and being brought this day guarded in front by a Troop of Horse and surrounded by Foot-Soldiers, who, taking them to the Dockside, did there string 'em up without further ado, leaving them to dangle as Warning to All, that the ships might carry the news of this Justice far and wide. I did note that two of them could scarce walk, being supported by their comrades; and learn from Mr. Nadauld that these two, being of better birth and Above the Others in Rank, were tortured with the Boot and the Thumbscrews that the Authorities might learn whether they had any Accomplices in Other Ships; but that naught was learnt thereby, the Rascals either having no Allies, or else Very Obdurate; and so all were hanged, and Justice was Avenged. The seaman whose ear I removed afflicted with a curious Twitching of His Face; do pray that this be not an Augury of Future Distemper.

June 21.

Sunday, and service on deck, and Commander Hamilton to pray both for the wounded departed and for safe Conduct to the Indies, where we sail I gather next week. My sailor with the Ear found paralysed this morning along the whole length of his body; so to Mr. Nadauld in some Perturbation of mind; who coming did say that these Paraplegia Dolorosa resulting from pressure of Traumatic or Bodily Substances upon the Spinal Marrow and Vital Centres of the Fount of Animal Spirits seldom did well; and so to bleed and purge him—this last especially important in such cases, for the Animal Spirits ceasing to control efficiently the Sphincters the body may become choked with Humoral Detritus—and to blister his Poll and all along the course of his Spine; sponging his head with Vinegar before blistering it; and so to leave him, and with Mr. Narauld to the Great Cabbinn, where my Senior did acquaint Commander Hamilton with what had occurred; and he much put out thereat, saying that he was hoping that our Wounded were now All on the Mend; and to bid us do all that Art suggested, and to inform him in two days of our Luck; and so I back to the unhappy wight and to bid Barlow and a Powder Boy take it in turn to Watch over him.

The bay all Phosphorescent tonight with little Spangles that did catch the Hawser ropes and oars dipped in the water till they looked as though they ran with Saint Elmo's fire; a most curious Phenomenon, one again I think needing Mr. Kelly his Microscope for Elucidation.

June 22.

The paralysed sailor no better this morning; his mouth drawn down at the corner so that he Mumbles instead of Articulates when he speaks, and Slobbers his Vittles like a Baby. Mr. Nadauld to view him, and we did examine the site of the wound; I informing him of that Sequestrum that did come away; and he pressing the bone about the area did say that it felt Thin, and moreover on his pressure a quantity of bloody serum oozed forth; and then after some discussion we did agree that Desp'rate Ills need Desp'rate Remedies; and so to remove him to the Cockpit; where having first dozed him with Rum to exalt his Fortitude and Numb his Emotions, we laid him out on the table and cleared away all the Muck over the wound, and then Mr. Nadauld did Trepann him, using for this purpose the Carpenter's bit, his own Trephine being stiff with Rust; having first Deflected the Skin with one of my Iv'ry handled Lancets. On his easing the Cut Part there did rush forth more of the aforesaid serum; and Mr. Nadauld gently lancing the Membranes we obtained more blood and some quantity of milky pus. But the Tabula Vitraea of that portion he removed was all discoloured and stank foully; so that Mr. Nadauld was in two minds whether to replace it, saying that it might be as well to leave a Hole for Drainage, a Cloaca as it were; but then replaces it after cleaning it and all about with sea-water; inserting however a tent in the skin, stitching it in place; and so the sailor was taken back to his hammock, never having moved at the first incisions, but fainting when Mr. Nadauld opened the Membranes. We did then bleed him in both arms some twenty ounces, and threw up a clyster of Gamboge and Jalap eight grains; and prepared a draught of half an ounce of Epsom Salts in Buckthorne Water to be given when he was recovered from his swoon; that his Guts might be scoured of all Harmful; then to cup him on the back and blister his head at the crown; and so, having done all that Science demands and Art could suggest to view the other patients; all doing well. I went with my Senior to see Mr. Rose and the Marine Officer; Mr. Rose has now risen from his bed (or, as a sailor, as I should say, His Bunk) and now takes the Air on Deck, his arm in a sling. The Marine Officer of course not risen, nor will be for some good fortnight yet; but his ancle does mend apace, and Mr. Nadauld bleeds him daily and feeds him on fruit to Oppose Fever, so that he is as comfortable as one expects.

Our prizes sold today at the Docks and fetch'd a good price; many of our men having been busy since we arrived scouring their decks and making all sweet again, also the Masts and Rigging whole and trusty. Both ships I hear were infernally Lousy; a contrast to our Navy vessels where under the rigorous discipline and deliberate cleanliness observed such Vile Insects are kept down; lice and fleas lurking only in such crannies as the Officers' bunks and the shelves of the Cook's galley; whilst Cockroaches are only to be found in abundance in the sailor's quarters in the Foc'sle.

Have been ashore today, and was very glad to stretch my legs; took a glass of very good wine in an

Inn called by some Jaw-twisting Portugee name—one of the Saints, I believe.

June 23.

The seaman operated on yesterday dead this morning, having Passed so quietly that his mates did not know he was sped until they called him; when receiving no answer they to look at him and found All his Face as Smooth as the Half of it was yesterday; when Barlow calls me, and I came in haste to find him cold and stiffening. So today he was taken out in the Long-boat and committed to the Deep beyond the bar the Authorities not permitting bodies to be sunk in the bay for fear of a Plague; these Islands being Volcanic, and there being some absurd rumour that whenever the sea-bottom should rise men sunk there will to their feet and Stalk Aweful through the Towns and Villages spreading Death and Pestilence; there being surely a Paradox here, since the same Natives that do inform one of this Pretty Tale do also assure one that the Hugest of Crabs live in the Port that will eat the flesh from off of a man's bones; so that surely, should any Ghost arise thus, he will be Most Infernally in Tatters. And so the seaman has died, and I doubt not that he has had a Merciful Release; though all our Labours have gone for Naught.

My mind Distracted from this theme after dinner by the sight of two Spanish ladies coming aboard;

they very pretty, and members of the Governor's household, he sending them when Commander Hamilton informs him of the plight of the Marine Officer and Mr. Rose; they being attended by a Footman and a little Negro page most comic, and coming in a Barge with six oarsmen all in gold and green Uniforms; so that I and Ned Tollit, to whom I was speaking at the time, did think Royalty was coming aboard; it is now tolerably certain that these my two patients will mend apace, there being few medicines so Stimulating as the sight of a Pair of Pretty Eyes all Moist with Pity. Ned Tollit laughs as Mr. Rose bows them below; saying that the Officers ever were Cosseted, and why did the Commander not send off also a brace or two of doxies for the Poor Dogs of Sailors? saying that on this his most dreary Watch he could pass Time Tolerably well even with the Fat Old Negress that sells apples on the Quay? and more to the same effect; at which I did laugh heartily, and quizzed him for a Man of Fickle heart; reminding him of yester afternoon, when I did stumble across him in an Arbour embracing with a pert little Portugee, and of that first time I did see him at Blackstakes with the landlord's daughter on his knee; at which he laughs again, and says that a Seaman must ever take his pleasure where he finds it, never knowing from day to day whether he may see that day's end. Wrote a letter to George Blumenfield and my other friends, assuring Mr. Pope that I had not forgot his request for a Mermaid and that as soon as I could secure one I would place her in a Barrel of Sea-Water and send her to him.

V

June 25.

Was ashore all day yesterday on a most enjoyable little Expedition with Mr. Nadauld and the First Marine Officer. After breakfast Commander Hamilton did come out on the Poop with all his Officers and caused the Ship's Company to be summoned, which done he did make a little speech thanking them one and all for the Manner in which they had supported him, especially in this late Encounter with the Pirates; and this done to say that he had made a good sale of their Two Prizes; and so, Ned Tollit blowing his whistle and two seamen running to bring a table from the Great Cabbinn, he did seat himself at it, and the Purser shared out the money, to each man his appointed share; I receiving to my great delight no less than Forty Two Pounds! at which I was greatly uplifted; and so, when all was done, Mr. Nadauld, who has been growing in kindness to me these latter days, to approach me and say that the Marine Officer, as a Commander of a Land Troop, did wish to ride a horse again; that he was to join him, as he wished to see something of the interior of the island; and that if I wished I could join them, the only thing needful being that

I could manage a Horse; which being country bred I was of course accustomed to. And so it was agreed; I did obtain Leave of Absence from our Captain, and then to the Carpenter in haste, to get him to sew me squares of leather on the seat of my new cord breeches, that my hams might not be chafed from the saddle; and so with my companions to the Cutter, which put us ashore, the Marine Officer (Mr. Butler) having already caused horses to be got ready for us at a Posada, or Inn; he having brought a Fowling Piece, for there are Partridge and other similar game in the Island; he not wearing his uniform, but a simple brown shooting coat and tops; so that on glancing at him, and then at Mr. Nadauld, he wearing a physician's tie-wig and dark blue coat and black breeches I did almost fancy myself at home again, going with my uncle to see some field that a farmer desired to show us.

We rode out of town and for near two hours were climbing, up gentle slopes that lie beneath the breast of the Great Mountain of the Island—that which the natives call the Pico Ruivo, the Red Peak. The ground all about this is very hilly, and gashed with many ravines that run down to the sea, forming harbours for the boats of the Fisher Folk. We wound up through these, getting somewhat hot and sweaty, there blowing a dry wind out of the East; the ravines all clustered with strange Trees and Palms, with little streams trickling down between them very quaint; and so we came out to a Plateau whence we had splendid views, the Prospects really Most Entrancing; we could see the distant islets of the Sail Rock and even to Bugio, so that by straining my eyes I could almost see that Bloody Spot where we fought the Pirate. Then a partridge—or some similar bird—got up from almost beneath our feet and Mr. Butler grabs his Piece, but the bird was gone, and naught but green Canary Birds twittering at us, which did exasperate him; and so we urged our horses on till we came out on another and larger clearing, where there was a mule track and two natives walking down it wearing their strange native hats; that called the Corapuca, being of stiff blue felt with a peak at the center; but Mr. Butler not in any way interested thereat, as a large brown partridge was clucking from the other side of the road; at which he urges his horse at it, and as it gets up fires off his gun at it and brings it down; and the natives bolt into the Shrubs at the side of the road for fear he is some great Lord; so that Mr. Butler getting off his horse in great good humour to pick up the bird throws them a coin, at which they come out from their Hidie hole calling down blessings on us.

And so we rode for an hour or more Mr. Butler getting one or two partridges and some conies, and very pleased thereby; we did also see a bird like a wood-cock and he shot at it but without avail. It was very enjoyable riding thus, for here on the hill summits it was cooler and the wind refreshing; we were always moving inwards towards the central core of hills, and the land grew more cultivated as we advanced into the Estates of the Mogados or Landlords. We rode through two villages whose natives ran out to look at us, and then after passing the second, pulling up our horses whilst Mr. Butler drew bead on a cony, a handsome Don rides out of a little wood and speaks to us, asking what our business was; so we to tell him it was but a pleasant Excursion away from ship Duties; and so falling with him into Agreeable Converse, he did Invite us to his Father's house for Meat, and a Rest after our ride. He did lead us after some quarter hours riding through Groves of Oranges and Vines to a large white house set in the midst of a Garden all Glorious with brightly coloured flowers; and there calling a Negro Slave to take our horses, led us into the interior of the house, this built with large airy rooms very cool and pleasant after our dusty ride. We did find the Noble Lord within and he to greet us, rising with some difficulty and evidence of pain from his seat; at which I saw Mr. Nadault eye him keenly. Other members of the Family did also appear, namely the Mother a very Grand Dame in a flowered skirt and Lace Head-dress, and two daughters, these very pretty, their names being, so far as I could manage their Sibilant Tongue, Anna and Rosa; this last name very Apt, for both were dark, yet Rosa had a bloom in her cheeks the other lacked, so that her face glowed for all the world like a Dark Red Rose; and she speaking a few words of broken English, and I having a little of the Spanish language we did Converse together with Much Merriment, she being a Frolicsome and Light-Hearted Beauty. A Negro Butler brings in wine on a fine silver tray and I to toasting her Silently with my Eyes so that she blushed and then made eyes at me over the rim of her wine-glass, the Saucy Puss; and so we growing friendly, and I admiring the garden, we did slip away together for she to show me the Flowers, and the Estate, and a stream that ran through it with a rustic bridge, a most pretty conceit; and she to treating me as though I were her equal and not a poor wight of a penniless Surgeon's Mate; so that by the bridge finding her hand strangely in mind I did make bold to kiss her; which kiss she returned, so that my Heart was gladdened Mightily; but then runs away laughing, and I after her.

And so back to the house, to find the servants setting table and the Grand Dame to stare at me most suspicious and no signs of my friends; but presently Mr. Butler comes from an inner room and beckons me; and I going with him find Mr. Nadauld examining the Great Lord; his apothecary reckoning that he was afflicted with the Gout but Mr. Nadauld, a cunning Man and one with some knowledge of the Distempers of these Tropic Parts, to disagree thereat and to say that he had that complaint known to the Italians as Dengue, or what we call the Dandy Fever; it commencing with pains in the Joints, but then passing to a Fever accompanied by a Rash, with which may come Sort Throat and Pains in the Eyeballs; the Complaint running an Intermittent Course, but very seldom fatal; it is a Distemper I learn that affects all ages, and in only the young and the aged does it ever rise to a Destructive Furor. So Mr. Nadault to bleed the Noble Lord and then to desire him to have made up at the French Chymist in Fonchal certain Prescriptions, namely powders of Epsom Salts gently to ease the Bowels; powders of Peruvian Bark to abate the Fever; and a Wash of Belladonna Leaves and Marshmallows to draw the pain from the limbs; and so the Lord to thanking him most heartily, saying to his son who was standing by that it was a Lucky Day for the Household when he found us; and to curse the Apothecary and vow that he would break his cane about his shoulders the next time he Visited; and so we went to dinner, I sitting opposite Rosa and feeding my Soul with Love of her Prettiness at the same time that I filled my belly with the Excellent Meats with which the board was furnished; there being a profusion of dishes containing Roast Beef and Pig and Game, with Lettuces and Potatoes baked whole with spices; and fruit, and three kinds of wine from My Host's own Vineyards. He was mighty pleased with Mr. Nadauld and did ply him with many questions, most searching, about the Ague, and it's cause; apologising neatly for troubling a man of Physic at his Vittles with such subjects, but saying that time was short and Mr. Nadauld a man obviously well versed in Medicine, and so he would like his Opinions, many of his Labourers not being able to work so enfeebled were they with that Distemper.

So Mr. Nadauld with a smile to say that for his part he preferred the Italian name for Ague Mal Aria, as pointing to the seat of the complaint; it being always a sickness attacking those that lived in or about Marshy Lands where the Rank Vapours arising from the Bog did seize their joints with Pains and Whip their Blood to Fever; and so to say to the Noble Lord that once the Disease was established in a man little could be done to aid him, since though the Peruvian Bark did depress the Fever, the Distemper hid away in the Joints and so lurked until the Bark was got rid of out of the body; when it once more came forth to Riot in the sufferer's System; but that he might improve the general State of his slaves by seeing that their houses were built away from all boggy wet ground; and the Lord much impressed thereby, and to lay upon his son that he should straightway see that this was done; and so the Dinner finishing we did repair to the Salon where two Portugees played to us on the guitar and they going about their work Rosa and Anna to seat themselve at a Spinett; and we had much enjoyable Music, the Lord's son singing a very plaintive Love Song in Spanish, and Mr. Butler, who has a good voice, to cap this with Ben Jonson's "Drink to me Only with Thine Eyes" and then the ladies sang, each a song, and then a duet; and Mr. Nadauld was asked for a song, but having no voice did laughingly refuse; only being pressed did ask for a Fiddle and this being brought to my astonishment did play sundry beautiful airs, I never having thought him possessed of such Talent; the which should be Sufficient Lesson to me that other birds than those seen on the outside boughs lurk within a thicket; and so the afternoon passed until time came for us to Horse again; and vilely sad I was to leave this pleasant Oasis. The Noble Lord did offer Fee to Mr. Nadauld, but this he refused saying that he had more than Amply Been Repaid by the Warm Hospitality which he had enjoyed; adding that what he had done was little enough, and that a Physician was no true man of Physic unless he was ever ready to help the Infirm; which did remind me of the Pimply Youth's Speech anent the Brotherhood of Medicine; thinking though also that Mr. Nadauld had been in no great Hurry to assist the Flogged Seamen; handing them over to me; though this of course was possibly due for his Anxiety that I should Experience all possible Practice.

And so the horses were brought, all the Family assembling on the Porch to wish us God-Speed, saying that their House was ever open to us should we come that way again, and our Host shaking Mr. Nadauld's hand and adding that he trusted that one day he might see him settled as Physician in the Island, there being a Place for such a man as he; and as I was listening to them, someone catches my sleeve, and I turned to find Rosa at my elbow and she holding finger to lip for silence takes a dark red rose from her sash, and pressing it to her lips gives it to me and I took it and pressed it to mine, and then climbed into my saddle and so we rode off down the drive, I turning again and again to catch a glimpse of Rosa until the road bent and I could see only the roof of the house. I was most infernally Depress'd at the thought that I should never see her more, and am still, the more so as I learn today that our Fleet sets sail tomorrow for the Indies. Such alas is Life; a lonely pilgrimage that Man must tread by himself, enlightened by meetings with Comrades whose roads never run long with his. Have wrapped the Rose carefully between sheets of soft paper and pasted it at the end of this My Journal; repository of all my thoughts, and so fit Warder for this Latest treasure.

June 26.

Up very early this morning, awoken by the shrilling of Ned Tollit's whistle; the Squadron set sail at dawn out to the bosom of the limitless Oceans;

and may God have us all in safe keeping and bring us Safe to Port.

June 28.

Sunday; service on board all the ships; we could hear their hymns coming across the water very faint. Still very downcast in spirits; truly this business of Love is a Distemper that sucks all the heart from a Man.

July 2.

Little to enter in my Journal these days. The Trade Winds do blow lustily so that we have had one or two Running seas, and part of the Stern Gilding damaged thereby.

July 5.

Sunday; Commander Hamilton to thank Almighty God that the weather continues fair and to ask that the winds continue with us. We have passed the Canary Islands, saluting the Island of Teneriffe and its port of Santa Cruz with a Salute of ten guns, and so passing down the Straits between it and Grand Canary to stand out to the Cape Verde Islands.

July 6.

The Officer of Marines on deck today, the discharge from his ancle drying up and so he about with crutches; so that coming on deck Commander Hamilton did quiz him glancing at his foot all bound with Bandages and asking him whether he had the gout, saying that Excess of Wine was ever a bad thing for a Sailor. Mr. Rose's wound now closed, though still tender.

July 7.

Off the Island of Sao Vicente today. Tonight have dropped anchor in the fine harbour of Porto Grande. I am informed that the Canary Islands were by the Old Navigators regarded as the Division between the East and Western Worlds; so that now we are indeed separated from our kindly Old World with its Ancient Civilisations and in the Lobby of the New. But our new Harbour very like the Roads of Fonchal and I indifferent whether I be in Old or Freshly Discovered Territory, wishing heartily that I was back upon the slopes of the Red Peak with my darling; for such I do now call Rosa in my innermost heart. I fear me though that she will not bear my image in her heart as I do hers; one so beautiful must surely have other Suitors whose ardour will cloud the Mem'ry of the Poor Surgeon's Mate who so humbly adores her.

July 8.

Have been ashore today and bought me a new hat, and being somewhat fatigued will not write much tonight. That fool Mr. Duhamel has just come aboard foxed, all bloody from tumbling into the Cutter at the Dock side; so Mr. Nadauld has gone to attend him, he entreating him not to let "That Oaf of an Apothecary's Boy come near him," he never have forgot—nor forgiven me—for scouring his Guts that time he was given a Dunt by the Deserting Sailor; the purgative doing its work most thoroughly.

July 9.

Left Porto Grande this morning the Ship's Bell having struck the Sixth Hour. Water and all things needful were taken on board yesterday, and now today, the Ramillies leading with the Commodore flying his Broad Pennant, our Ram points East by South and East and East again; we are bound for the Lesser Antillies and the Island of Trinidad, and there has been much noise from the Foc'sle, singing of Ditties; the tall seaman very prominent bawling away thus:

In Plymouth Town there lived a maid—
Bless you, young women—
And.we had such a loving talk
I'll go no more a'roving, etc.

and, even more Scandalous, thus:

Once I had a Nigger girl and she was fat and lazy
Then I had a Spanish girl, she nearly druv me crazy
Way, Haul A-way, We'll haul away the bowlin, etc.

so that the Carpenter's arm has near been jogged off, and he has broke his fiddle string.

July 10.

The wind increased this day to a Gale, so that our ships became scattered, and some uneasiness has been felt concerning the new mast of the Mercury, though so far this has stood well. Mr. Duhamel has been very Sea-Sick at the motion of the ship, he being Officer of the Watch part of the day, and only now recovering from his Drunken Bout.

July 12.

The wind still continuing strong, it was found difficult to gather the crew for service, so none has been held. I have remained below in my bunk the greater part of daylight reading the Testament and then in my Sydenham.

July 13.

The wind has abated a little, but there continues such a Roll of the Sea that one could fancy that King Neptune was stirring below, stretching himself after a long sleep; such Mighty Billows, even as Ned Tollit did tell me of, that mount up and up till one can scarce see the sky for green water.

July 14.

The seas are still Dev'lish, and the poor wights of sailors have scarce any dry clothes or place to sleep, it being necessary I gather to keep our ship's bows to the Seas, but these continually breaking over the capstan so that oft the bows are invisible, the water sweeping towards the stern and invading the Hatches. The Officers in their Stern Cabbinns are not so badly off, but the Foc'sle runs with waters some of which have penetrated my cabbinn, and thereby soaked my night shirt and a fine new night cap. 'Tis grand though to see how Sternly our Ships do defy the Elements; all our Flotilla are still keeping company, the Ramillies riding the Ocean, despite the Waves, like a Sea-God, the Frigate and the Mercury not so happy, oft showing their strakes almost to the Keel, but yet persevering stubbornly in the wake of the Ramillies.

July 16.

The wind and the following sea still continue, though they are abating, for which may God be thanked. It has proved almost impossible these latter days even to take Meat for the Wild Capers of the ship; she is as uneasy as a Dog with Fleas, and her Antics as Curious. The Cutter was washed off the booms yesterday and was secured with ropes only just in time.

July 18.

The sun appeared through the cloud-rack this morning, and all were duly grateful. The Glass remains Steady so that even if the present wind continues no worse storm will follow. A seaman was knocked against the Aftermast at noon, losing his feet with the Dip of the vessel, and was carried below Stunned; and I to bleed him, and so he recovering to get him to his hammock for an hour or so to gather his Wits. I do trust that his scull be not injured; from my Infirmary days onward I do seem to have been unlucky with such cases.

July 19.

Sunday, and the boat being tolerably steady a service of representatives of the crew was held on deck. I see on looking back in my Journal that amongst the Interest of the days I have not placed on record that no trace was ever found of the Sloop the Dragon, so that it is feared that she is sunk with all her men, Captain, Officers, and Crew; unless she fled before the wind to make the Azores; and as I stood on the deck and looked out over the Wild Tumultuous Seas, I was unpleasantly reminded of what a Little secures us from such a Watery Fate. The seaman stunned yesterday whom I bled quite recovered; do trust that he will continue so.

July 21.

Sighted a Spanish Squadron of two Galleons and a Gun-boat, and to salute them with ten guns, they homeward bound.

July 22.

Sighted a school of sea-cows, those strange creatures that the Ancient Mariners did take for Water Human Beings, mermaids and mermen and the like; did not manage to secure one for friend Pope. We are now fringing the Edge of the Sailor's Graveyard, that Ghoulish Sargasso Sea in which in beds of weed Tall Ships are bound as with chains of Iron; and many strange stories thereby amongst the sailors. The wind continues with us, for which we are duly grateful.

July 23.

A case or two of dryness of the skin to me this morning in the Sick Bay, and I fear me that the scurvy is breaking out again. It is a curious Distemper, this; resultant one supposes upon the increasing of Sharp Salts in the blood from the absorbtion of Sea-Water through the skin. The men are well fed with salted meat and a little fresh; this last grows somewhat rank; and a sufficiency of green stuff, potatoes and the like. Bled them, to relieve the System of the surfeit of Humours, and purged 'em; I do wonder whether the state of their bowels has aught to do with the complaint, for they get most costive. Great quantities of weed passed us all day.

July 24.

Hailed a British brig bound for the Cape Verde Archipeligo. Other seamen to me today with this infernal scaliness of the skin; one has his gums very sore; there is no doubt that the scurvy is once more come amongst us. Even the officers are now affected, as I was informed by Mr. Nadauld, taking the air with him on the poop. Mr. Duhamel has got it; Mr. Butler he thinks is commencing with it; but curious, Mr. Rose and the wounded Marine Officer, also the Commander, have not; the first pair no doubt because as Invalids their Health has been well looked after; the last possibly because he is very fond of butter and eats large quantities of it, this greasiness of Temperament discouraging the Acrid Salts.

July 26.

No service today there being a long heavy swell on that makes it difficult to keep one's feet. A Marine broke his crown this day and a Sailor his arm through the latter falling on him on a Ratline rotted by the seas breaking; the seaman putting undue strain on it as the ship swayed; and some merriment thereat amongst the respective messmates of the sailor and marine. Neither are hurt bad; the Soldier was lurching away when struck, this and his stiff hat breaking the force of the sailor's tumble; and the seaman having a Clean Fracture of the Humerus near the elbow; fortunately not into the joint. Set it and fixed it with a Charge of tow and strips of canvas soaked in tar and gum.

July 28.

The seas do never abate. Even when quiet there is a long swell that rolls the ship solemnly to and fro as on a See-Saw. I do begin to understand the reason for the Mariner's Peculiar Gait. My sailor and the Marine hurt yesterday doing well; the Marine indeed has no more than a Contused Scalp and sundry bruises on Salient Angles of his Anatomy, and has already mostly forgot about them. Bled them both however for the good of their Health eight ounces. More scurvy cases to me, some bleeding at the nose; have applied the routine treatment, but this Distemper does seem to depend upon the fact that we are at sea for such lengthy periods and there is little one can do save to Endeavour to keep it within limits until land is reached and with its kindly fruits the balance of the Humours is once more Established. With Mr. Nadauld did inspect the Marine Officer's ancle, the swelling now all going away and but little discharge; but we thought it as well to leave the Tent in situ. The injury, lying as it does at the Malleolus of the Tibia just above its articulation with the Astragalus, is far too near the Crannies of the Ligaments for comfort; there being a risk that these become involved and so Inspissating fill the Metatarsal articulations with those Sharp Salts whose grinding causes the pain of the Screws or the Rheumatics. We did also bleed him and attend to his bowels, so that the body be not unduly oppressed in its efforts to repair the injury. He hobbles about with a stick, keeping company with Mr. Rose, who has now returned to light duties. Went a'angling today, to the Amusement of Commander Hamilton; caught some Mac'rel and other queer tinted fish whose name I do not know, a great Multitude of them; we had them for supper, and there being some over the aged Cook did make a hash of them with duff and a few potatoes for the Crew, and they were mighty grateful for the change.

July 31.

The Cook throwing overboard the heads and entrails of the fish I caught we have been followed these last days by two ugly brutes of sharks; so that today Commander Hamilton has been amusing himself by shooting at the vermin with a Musket, and has hit one, the other sheering off. Our Captain is too well versed in sea-lore to catch the brute and drag it on board; unlike your Obdt. Servant, who was Fool enough to wish to make cane of the Backbone and so obtaining one had after several days to throw it back into the Sea, its Odour being Intolerable.

August 2.

Sunday, and service on deck, there being a calm and warm sunshine. Lolled on deck in the afternoon, dividing my time Perfunctorily between reading my Testament, and in my Sydenham, and writing a letter to my uncle; this to be posted when we next Speak Ship or reach land. Looking round me at the great bowl of sea I did reflect that we had so long ago left land that we might imagine that there was no more left, and we doomed to sail on to the World's End, held ever fast despite our progress in a Watery Witch's Circle.

August 3.

Some welcome excitement today. The Ramillies leading did sight a half-sunk wreck, and to cleanse the rust out of her cannon opened fire on it, making flag that we should form into Battle Line and follow suit.

So the frigate swings about and the Mercury follows, and we follow the Mercury, and each as it passed the Derelict gave it a broadside; so that our ship once more quaked to the Thunder of our Artillery and the sea was clouded with gun-smoke. Twas droll to see one Powder Boy dropping a charge of powder and so being picked up by the Gunner and laid across the barrel of the third forrard piece the while one of the gun-crew laid on heartily with a piece of rope-end. Our shot did appear to have but little effect on the wreck, though its solitary mast was shattered; but as we left it behind us it did plunge suddenly to vanish for Ever beneath the waves; so that all were pleased that one more trap was broke for the safety of poor sailors.

August 4.

Land sighted due West some five leagues today; tis thought it is the North Point of the Island of Barbados. The sky, sunny in the morning, is now overcast, and the Officer of the Watch informs me that the glass is falling. I learn that we are now in the Hurricane Months these holding from about the middle of July to October; so that I do pray we make Harbour without meeting one of these Ferocious Gales.

August 5.

My hope of last night not it seems to be answered. All last night the wind, from moaning most eerie in the rigging, began to blow in little short gusts, so that the crew were rallied in haste to shorten sail. A long heavy swell was set up by the wind, so that betwixt the ship's roll and the rattle of the bare spars against the mast I got little sleep last night; and rose this morning to find the wind increased to Gale force, and the sea choppy and very threatening. So today the Ramillies, after bearing towards that distant peak of land, finding that the wind blew steadily out of the East and was like to drift her bulk on to the Lee Shore; to say naught of the similar danger to us other ships of her Flotilla, has made signal that we are to run South and thus as heretofore it is each for himself and we have been swept like leaves before the wind; the Gale rising to a Fury worse than that of the previous storm, which Lord knows was bad enough. All hands were busy early this morning making Fast all moveables on the deck, and this afternoon the ship pitching very bad I and Ned Tollit have deemed it wise to lash the sailor with the broken arm in his hammock so that he break no more of his bones.

August 7.

It has been impossible to write in my Journal latterly, the Ship plunging like a mad thing. The wind has veered to the North, but still blows with a Horrific Fury, the Cutter was stove in yesterday by the seas; the Commodore has flagged all ships to make for Trinidad. We passed today the Northernmost of the coralline islets of the Grenadines, and gave them a wide berth; these seas are shallow, and such islands thus treacherous ports for poor wights of sailormen. Do see why we were ordered to run South; these Hurricanes have custom to swing half-circle wise, and the wind that carries us now South (and will with God's aid enable us to beat round the North of Trinidad) would have Bashed us on the cliffs of Barbados had we attempted to beat round the Capes of that Island.

August 9.

Sunday, and the wind abating, though the heavy seas continue. The Ramillies grounded this afternoon on one of the Grenadines and is still ashore. No service; wedged myself in my bunk, read my Testament, and prayed for Safety and a Passage to Calm Anchorage.

August 10.

Today, we beating about to keep touch with the Ramillies, she throwing overboard sundry of her heavy ordnance, puncheons of water, spars and an anchor, to lighten herself, she being still aground; a great Sea swept our decks and carried away Mr. Duhamel, so that he has no more been seen. Thus tonight all are sorrowing, for though as a Man he was unpleasant, yet as a Sailor he Died in the Performance of His Duty, and so is worthy of Ranking with the Mighty Heroes of Antiquity.

Tonight there has been firing of cannon; the Ramillies has got herself off, and is firing guns to recall the Flotilla; though the Frigate is far down on the Horizon, only her masts showing.

August 11.

The Ramillies grounded again this morning, being carried on the Lee shore by the swell. All our sailors and those of the Mercury have been very busy getting Ropes aboard her with intent to pull her afloat again; and the Barge, carrying these Hawsers across, has twice been upset in the seas, these being very choppy; so that two seamen have been drowned.

Commander Hamilton at the third attempt served the crew out a measure of Grog, so that they reached the Ramillies and we setting sail with the Mercury towed the Ramillies off and into deeper, safer waters: and our Main Sail has split, the wind being uncommonly gusty.

The barge has this moment returned with one of its crew with a cracked poll and the helmsman with a sprained knee; so no more tonight, but must to the Cockpit to attend them.

August 12.

More risky work today getting some casks of water and other provision aboard the Ramillies to replace those that her complement threw overboard. Two casks were stove in as they were lowered into the barge, this being thrown up against the Lancaster's side by the seas, which do continue to run high. I did see very distant the white smother of breakers against the shores of that island on which the Ramillies grounded, and very thankful thereby that it was not us who had gone ashore. The Ramillies somewhat strained by her grounding, and her pumps have been working all this day.

August 13.

Sighted the coast of Trinidad after supper tonight; we shall reach land none too soon, for the scurvy increases, and our water grows foul.

August 14.

Still at sea. The land thought to be Trinidad sighted yesterday naught but one of the chain of Grenadines, and much annoyance thereat. We would have attempted to go ashore for fresh Water and Green Meat, but the wind is against such a Manoeuvre.

August 15.

Land again sighted to the South this morning, a Continent that fills most of the Horizon; so that it is surely Trinidad at last. The Sailors very Cheered thereat; most of them, when the weather permitted (there has been a continual Drizzle the last two days) perching themselves in the Rigging staring at the land as though it was some curiosity; and much Singing, and dancing of Jigs, Hornpipes, Reels, and the like, the which have oft been strangely interrupted by the Rolling Heave of the vessel, this throwing dancers and musician together in a heap under one of the bulwarks; not that any were thereby in any degree Discommoded.

August 16.

A blessed peace today; calm waters and a soft breeze blowing off the land laden with many Strange Intoxicating Odours. We have cruised along the coast, and I have marvelled to see the dimpling shades of the water, these being very shallow; and the schools of gaily coloured fish, and those that fly with their fins, one leaping right against our bows this noon; and, through the spy-glass, the tall palms and ferny trees of the land, with many Imps of Monkeys playing amongst their fronds, and gaily coloured birds, some about the size of starlings and their plumage like a Sultan's robe; which Ned Tollit informs me are called Macaws; and others so small at this distance I can only detect their presence by sudden Flashes of Light from the Iridescence of their Plumage, these being called Humming Birds; and Ned Tollit to inform me that these have beaks so shaped that they can feed on the honey of the flowers even as the Bee doth; but as to this, having a mind to that he told me of how a Shark's Backbone would make a Fine Cane, I am somewhat dubious, and shall Preserve an Open Mind till I can resolve the Matter for myself. He also told me that these Islands, beautiful as they are, are in Proportion the Home of many Vile Wild Beasts, snakes and the like; also of that Strange Beast the Tarantula, whose bite doth cause folk to dance and sing; but as to this I am again Preserving an Open Mind; resolving to obtain one of these aforesaid Tarantula and try its sting on some animate creature; perhaps a Marine or Sailor, or a Slave (I hear these are cheap) or failing these one of the Goats that still live a Troglodyte existence in the Hold; these looking most infernally Doleful, worse even than the usual manner of Goats, so that they might welcome some Physic that would enliven their Hearts. On reflection I do see that it would be difficult to detect the effect of the bite on a Sailor, at least; these having been quite frantic since we sighted land, bawling Songs and Huzza-ing so that the Foc'sle has been a Bedlam.

August 17.

This afternoon we came in sight of a Cape carrying a small fort and did salute it with fifteen guns and the running up of our Ensigns to the fore-peak, and so turned South-West, two Islands lying before our Ram.

August 18.

Hove to during the night, the passage of this Strait—the Dragon's Mouth—which leads us to our Harbour the city called Port of Spain being tricky in the present prevailing winds. Today have sailed slowly between Monos Isle and one with a Most Tongue Twisting name, to wit—Chacachara Island—though I have copied this from the chart I am not wholly certain that I have got its spelling right, some wight having killed a cockroach on the map and so given the portrayed Island a shape surely never intended by the Surveyors. Tonight we have let go the anchor outside the Roads.

August 19.

Today we rove up the anchor and moved into berths in the Harbour; I have seldom heard the soldiers sing with such Vehemence as they did this morning at the Capstan; there is a feeling of deep Satisfaction abroad that though once again we have been blown out of direct course we have reached safe Harbourage without undue Mishap. The Ramillies has been towed ashore and beached, to have her bottom timbers attended, these being badly scraped by her going ashore. I hear that we also are to be towed ashore, that our keel may be cleansed of the worms and sea-wrack that attach themselves thereto in such a voyage as ours. The Admiral of the Port has been out to pay his respects to the Commodore and with him the Port Surgeon to see whether we have any infectious diseases aboard. Did catch a glimpse of this worthy as he came aboard: he and all with him were yellow as guineas with the Yellow Fever, that dread scourge of these Tropic Parts; that which with the Malarial Fever saps all the heart out of Europeans within a space of a few years, so that they become shrunk-fleshed and jaundiced, and soon die; thus these Islands are for all their wild beauty a Treacherous Paradise. The sailors were anxious, as were all, to get ashore and feel firm Earth beneath their feet; but this they were not permitted, for much has to be done to get the ship ready for beaching; the Yards stepped, the

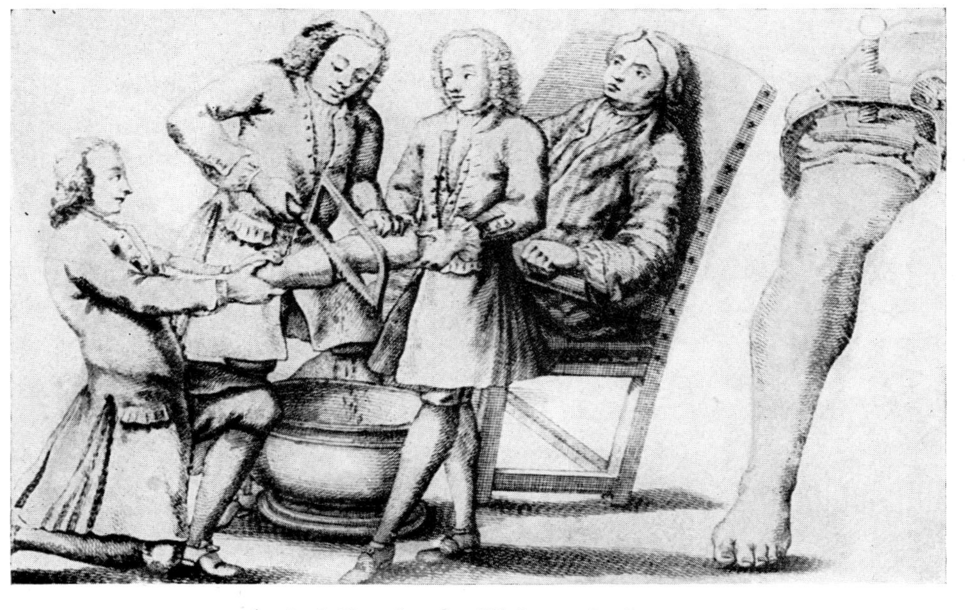

Amputation in the Eighteenth Century

Ropes stowed away, the Cannon dismounted and lowered by tackle to flat barges that will take them to the Ordnance Yard; and the Marines set to cleaning their muskets and repairing the stocks.

As the Surgeon's Mate however there was little for me to do, so after warning the Cook to get plenty of Green Stuffs and fruit aboard for the Scurvy Men I went ashore with Mr. Nadauld and viewed the town; it being most Infernally Warm, the temperature registering eighty-three in the Shade, so that at this our first landing from the cold freshness of the ship we were soon tired, and glad to rest awhile in an Inn by the Sea-Front, where we took our Ease and a glass of wine and viewed the Harbour and the many ships lying at anchor there; and Mr. Nadauld to discourse on that strange Lake of Pitch that is to be found in the South of the Island, of its extent, and how the largest and most powerful of beasts tumbling therein are held fast, and so sink, their bones entombed for all ages like the bodies of the Ancient Pharaohs; and from this, I plying him with questions concerning that Universal Prophylactic hitherto prepared from the bodies of the Ptolemies and Egypt Kings, he did smile, and remark that though he would not dispute the Authority and Testimony of Men Past, yet to his mind any small virtue that lay in such things was due to the pitch with which their bodies were soaked; this having a Loosening Action on Phlegmatick Humours and being Antidote to Foul Morbidities by virtue of its Acridness; and so finding him in a Tolerant Mood to ask him concerning that strange Mania resulting from the bite of the Tarantula Insect; and here he did inform me that the Mania was only one of those Deliriums that are caused by any bite of Animal where Foreign Substances are injected into the Body, and spoke of the Dancing Manias that grievously afflicted the world in Mediaeval Times; these arising from a Hysteria akin to that of an Over-Wrought Woman, brought on by the Wars and Pestilences of that time, and recovering only on being fiddled to so that they Danced till they Dropped; the vulgar of the time attributing them to the bite of Insects and not to the Real Cause; so that this Strange Fantasy did thus Arise. Mr. Nadauld is plainly a man of much knowledge and thought; I must listen to him and follow all that he shows me with closest attention.

August 20.

Have been on shore again today; small Tug Boats have warped us to the dockside, so that now one can step straight off our planks to the shore; a rather delightful sensation. The Lancaster has been pulled over by strong ropes at a steep angle so that her bilge straking is exposed; the List makes it somewhat difficult to move about, and sundry of the Officers have taken lodging ashore until such time as the boat is restored to her normal keel, amongst them Mr. Nadauld. I and the crew have however had to stay on board. Leave has freely been granted me however; so today I have been ashore since immediately after breakfast, roaming in the sunny streets of the Port and through them out into the country beyond, much diverted by the strange medley of types and costumes I encountered. The country beyond grows wild very sudden; there is a narrow suburb of merchants' houses, and some plantations of Sugar and Tobacco, and then the edge of an impenetrable forest, very threatening and mysterious; it is here termed a Jungle, and extends for long miles across the centre of the island.

The trees are like Giant Ferns, some, called Palm Trees, very tall; teeming with life, bright coloured birds, and little brown Apes, that chatter worse than the French Woman, and run together in packs like a School of Fish. Ate several oranges today, the taste of them still lingers.

August 21.

Saw my first Leper today, and vastly Intrigued thereby. The way of it was this. I was in a wide lane opening off the City's Main Street this morning, examining some quaint globular spiked fish, when a Negro who was at the same stall chaffering for certain herbs gives a groan and says "De Lord hab Mercy On Us!" and so dropping to all fours, disappears beneath the rugs with which the Counter was draped. I turning to see the cause of his Alarm did find the street emptying fast, and down the middle of the road a Poor Devil of a man walking, his face all grey and puffy and eaten away with great Ulcers so that he could surely only have seen men dimly, "As Trees Walking." He was in Rags, and his legs and feet were swollen, the toes of one foot all gone so that he shuffled in the dust; the cur-dogs snapped and bit at his heels, and to protect himself from their worrying he carried a thick staff in a hand from which three fingers had rotted away; the other hand the right was naught but a vile Ulcer that had rotted away the Metacarpals right down to the wrist, so that the bones protruded. He stank most horribly, though this I think not so much from his Distemper as his General State. All fled at his approach, and I did wish to do likewise, but remembering certain things that Mr. Nadauld told me concerning this Disease of Leprosy I did hold my ground until he was within a few yards of me; when my courage failed me, and I fled behind the Stall, throwing a piece of money to him and calling out that I had done so; when he stops, bends to the earth and searches till he had found the money, and then stands erect again and a hideous grimace passed across his face that I took it he intended for a smile; he opened his mouth to give thanks, but naught issued but a husky gurgling and croaking; and so he passed on his way, I somewhat reproaching myself that I had lost courage; but there, he was too far gone in his Complaint for the cleverest of Physicians to aid him. There is nothing left for him now to hope for but a swift end out of his torment.

This Distemper of Leprosy, though this is the first example I have seen of it, is not in any way a Disease peculiar to these Climes. It is to be found in all countries of the world, in hot places and Temperate, in Europe and such Continents and Isles as those we are now amongst; being again a Universal Disorder, for Explorers have found it in the most remote of Territories, ravaging the natives; there is no doubt that it is one of those complaints of Nutrition, which by persistent Tipping of the Humoral Balance finally drive the body to a Distracted State where in its efforts to throw out the Morbid Quantities it commences to break down and as it were to Feed Upon itself, so that the Body Corporal Decays even while the Immortal Soul inhabits It. There are Lepers still in England now, and of ancient times they were as common as Ague cases are today; their diminution of numbers resulting of course from the improvement in Diet and Social Conditions resultant upon our High Degree of Civilisation; in such spots as these Tropic Islands, where the primitive savage conditions still obtain, the disease of course flourishes. It is one of those Originally Cutaneous Complaints, similar to the Icthyosas or Fish Skin diseases and that Gangrene which comes from over-indulgence in Rye Bread (this again points to its Alimentary Origin). It is not therefore, as Theory would suppose and Experience teaches, an Infectious complaint; nor one that in the early stages is Contagious; though when the Lesions appear, should matter from these be implanted upon the Tenderer portions of the Body, such as the Mucous Membrane of the Mouth, these may be disturbed and so the body as a whole be Infected with Horror, and blindly unreasoning try to throw hence all such matter; recoiling Aghast so that Mortal Injury is done to Health, the skin breaks down from its efforts, forming the Ulcers that never heal; and that Slow Decay sets in from which only Death may give respite.

Thus, as one would suppose from its origin, it may be divided into three stages; One, that in which the body first stirs itself, there is Malaise and Fever, the presence of the Morbid Humours shown by red Patches and Eructations on the skin; Second, that in which the skin grows Desperate, warts and nodules appearing that break down to form Ulcers; Third, that final Miserable Condition in which Decay sets in, the digits and even limbs Rotting Off, and the skin Dying so that it appears grey, puffy, and scaly; in this last condition the Sufferer may live for ten or Fifteen years, his Vital Functions in no way grievously impaired; he experiences hunger and feels cold; though few except those similarly affected will then minister to him; the soul is loathe to leave his stinking carcase until Blow is Struck at the Vital Centres in Heart or Brain or Lung; the complaint being Alimentary in origin these are not often affected, becoming so only in the Last Stages, when the Vitality droops beneath the poor sufferer's Miserable Outcast Condition; I have heard of one Spanish Captain who would shoot all such with his Pistol, and, faith, though, there be those who would stand aghast at this man's assumption of the Prerogatives of God, yet there is much to be said for his action; these creatures must surely at the last pray for a quick ending; though again it is possible, that God being all Merciful Nature provides for them in proportion to their distemper Compensation that we know not of.

Certain it is that the Disease is one greatly to be feared, more even than the slow Gangrene of an Injured Member; for here the Distemper is limited to a Single Surface only, and may be relieved by Excision; but Leprosy being a Universal Inherent Complaint more Insidious than the Small Pox is incurable, and one affected must skulk through the rest of life barred from all friendly human concourse; thus there was excuse for the Terror of the Negro, for the poorer classes in proportion hold fast to the few poor Carnal Pleasures of Human Intercourse being from their Station denied the Gentler Arts; Gluttony and Lust their sole Relief from Tedium, and ever desperate even of losing these Earthly Pleasures. It does Deeply Stir the Mind to meet with such cases. Thought is again directed to the Inner Meaning of Disease; surely not everyone is afflicted for his sins; frequently he is afflicted for those of his ancestors, as seen in the Gout; perhaps this problem is one reason why Our Blessed Lord visited this world; man having, shall we suppose?, reached a stage of Mental Development when such things were beginning to be considered by the Philosophers; our Lord coming then to point that all such were in the Hands of God, and that whether a man was diseased or no, if he lived a Godly Life he should receive Reward out of all Proportion to his Travail. I am sensible that I am venturing on very Dangerous Ground; these things have been debated by those with Mightier Intelligences than mine all through the ages; yet as Disease is found on study to be a Simple enough thing resting on certain Surmises, so these problems may be simple enough to be resolved by those with small Wits, if they are humble and believe that God never sets an Insoluble Problem.

I am tired; my brain flags; no more tonight. I will to bed.

August 22.

Have been ashore again today. It is impossible indeed to rest on board for the thump of the carpenters hammers and the screech of their saws, and the smell from the keel where the Caulkers are burning the weeds and slime from our strakes with smouldering tow. All are very busy at work, for the Admiral is anxious for us to set sail again, we being overdue at Barbados.

August 23.

Sunday; the ship still being careened, with Mr. Nadauld and Messrs. Butler and Rose, Ned Tollit, and seven seamen and four Marines to service at the Great Cathedral. The worship Popish, but very impressive, the Church lofty and dim, the walls hung with sea-trophies, and armour and banners, and model ships hanging from the roof trees; these last presented by sundry Mariners grateful for Delivery from the Dangers of the Ocean. The church very full of soldiers and sailors of all nations, and numerous Great Ladies; the complexions and costumes of these did remind me Dismally of my Rosa; I wonder where she be now, and whether in her prayers today she remembered the lank Surgeon's Mate? Ah me, Life is a very pleasant but also confoundedly queer thing. Dined with the officers after at an Inn, and gamed with them; took a stroll with Mr. Nadauld in the country in the afternoon; but it coming on to rain, we did return to the same Inn for supper, whence I have but lately returned.

August 24.

The Lancaster on an even keel again tonight, for which I am grateful. First she was pulled over to the right; and just as one had become accustomed to that particular list, three days ago she was pulled on her left side; and one had to readjust one's balance all over again. It is still impossible to rest aboard her however, except at night; stores and the Ordnance are now coming aboard, and there is much work also on the Rigging and Spars. After breakfast had one case of a Workman stabbed in the knee; he having been hurt in a quarrel with another workman over some woman or other; these Dons are ever ready to draw steel, though their Anger Evaporates as soon as it Arises. It has rained all day again, most dismal; the Jungle on the Hills behind is all smoking and steamy.

August 25.

Quantities of Provisions coming aboard today, with casks of powder and puncheons of water; an Augury of our Near Sailing. An English Merchant Ship came into Harbour today, all battered from a storm she encountered beating up round the North of the Island; she was to have made Port near Baia where the Pitch Lake is, but was prevented by the heavy swell following the wind; so I hear that the Commodore has altered his Plans, and we are to sail out through the Dragon's Mouth, following the same course as that by which we entered Harbour, but in the reverse direction. Like not this mention of storms; have had a Surfeit of them; and too they are rendered Extra Dangerous by the Shallowness of these Seas, the Coral Insects building Reefs that run far out from the land.

August 26.

My last trip ashore today. Tomorrow we sail for Barbados; and I trust that this Effort may be more successful than the last. As we shall not visit here again I have bought me sundry little Mementoes in the Shape of Three Curios, viz:

A fish carved out of coral very cunning, for my uncle.

A fine Spanish shawl for my aunt.

A dried coffer fish with a sucker mouth, painted quaintly in the manner of his original colouring. This last I have hung with cord from the wall of my cabbinn; it imparts to it quite a Nautical Air.

VI

August 27.

The Ramillies fired a gun today at dawn, and all the ships of our Fleet roused thereby and very busy about getting up the anchor and shaking out the sails. We sailed without mishap an hour before breakfast, and we sat down to that meal with the ship already rolling to the swell without the bar. After breakfast I to the Cockpit, and found sundry cases of Surfeit of Drink awaiting me, there having been much swilling of Farewell Libations by the seamen last night; two came aboard very foxed, and were hustled below by their mates before they were seen by Commander Hamilton. These last two still being in somewhat of a Daze I bled and purged; the others I merely purged. The wind blows strong tonight, and our ships are hard put to it to keep off the Land, the wind being on the weather bow, its direction almost due East.

August 28.

Today the wind has risen to Gale force; this morning dawned to reveal us off the Island of Monos with the isle of Chacachara on our lee; but the wind proving so vehement we have been unable to lose 'em, and have passed the day tacking to and fro up the Channel. Tonight they are passing astern; but the seas are running high, and the Glass is falling; we are like to find Heavy Weather out in open Waters.

August 29.

Great firing of guns late last night, the Ramillies passing from the shelter of the Land to receive in open seas the full blast of the Gale, and so nearly going ashore, firing guns to acquaint us of her position, so that we might keep near her. The wind still very strong today, swinging round in most Exasperating Fashion; as it was yesterday it would have been of help, but now it blows, not East, but North-North-East, and we are making but small progress.

August 30.

Sunday, and I for one to pray for better weather. The Gale now screaming out of the East, and the frigate has lost her Sprit Sail Yard thereby. Seas have been pouring over our decks, making a Service impossible.

September 1.

On deck this morning for Air to find the Ramillies hull down to the North, firing guns for us to follow her; none of the other ships visible. After dinner sighted the Mercury, making heavy weather, far distant on the port bow. No new cases; have laid in my bunk the greater part of the day, reading in my Sydenham; which treatise is becoming somewhat worn, the seawater bringing the calf off the back.

September 2.

We have lost our position. It has not been possible to make an observation these latter days, the sun being obscured by drifting rain clouds. Still no sign of the Ramillies, but the frigate and the Mercury are still with us; she cannot be far away. The wind is abating, but the sea is still queasy, with a most infernal slow roll.

September 3.

We lost a poor wight of a seaman today, he dropping from the Main Yard at a sudden dip of the ship, to plunge into the water and be no more seen. It is to be hoped his plunge deprived him of breath so that he drowned immediately; there are overmany sharks in these warm seas for one to linger in consciousness. The clouds have cleared; today has been very hot. Without understanding the half of the jargon of the officer of the Watch, I learn that we are far off our course; but, faith, this was scarce news to me or to any of us; and I am becoming accustomed to such information.

September 4.

Some excitement at mid-morning at the sighting of land; this turning out later to be naught but a miserable little Coral Isle, small enough to carry only five palm trees; what I understand is termed An Atoll. But warning that vastly more of the land than could be seen was present was given by lines of breakers shattering themselves on reefs far out to sea; it is to be hoped that the Ramillies has not been wrecked on such a Dismal Spot. It is reckoned by the Officers that this islet is indication that we have been blown amongst the Testigos Isles and some merriment thereat, for we are, if this is true, as far or farther from our Destined Port in Barbados than we were when we left Port of Spain. A Marine came to me today with a fever and some aching in his loins; I think me that the fool has catched a Lues Venerea. Bled him; purged him with ten grains of Jalap and cupped him over the pains.

September 6.

More rain and wind today. We are caught within a veritable girdle of tiny coral islands. Mr. Nadauld has catched a Rheum; to minister to him, and then he being somewhat feverish and keeping his couch, I to Commander Hamilton's great Cabbinn, he having twisted his ancle coming off Watch. Found him seated before a brazier his leg stuck out on a chair in front of him, his head bound in a Bandanna kerchief and six wigs steaming on their stands arranged in a circle about the fire. His ancle not sprained in any way badly; did desire him to rest for that day and keep a Compress steeped in sea-water about it, and it would most probably be whole on the morrow. The wind has dropped tonight; there is something of a calm. All ships have furled sail and cast out a sea-anchor, lest in the absence of wind we drift on to the reef of one of the Coral Isles.

Later; I open this my Journal to note that we have recently been passed by a barque with very tall masts and white sails, standing across the three ships of the Squadron North-North-East. She carried no Riding Lights, and was only detected by the frigate on the moon coming out from behind a cloud and silvering her rigging; the frigate promptly fired a gun, but the ship was past, to disappear as the moon went behind a cloud, to reappear off our lee as the moon shone forth again. She replied neither to hails nor the firing of shotted cannon, and there are wild tales flying round amongst the sailors that she was naught else but that grim craft the Flying Dutchman, and that therefore this cruise will end in disaster. I have little faith in these tales, but the ship as she glided ghost-like across the path of the moonbeams might well have been taken for no earthly craft, but one fashioned by Dead Men at the World's End. Certain it is that our Journey so far has been Tedious and Exhausting, but this is surely due to the Uncertainty of the Elements rather than to any Supernatural Agencies (though these matters are in the Hand of God). The crew of the Flying Dutchman, whether they be Spektres or Real Men, would be of interest to a Physician, since the story runs that the Yellow Fever broke out on the original Ship, and she was forced to sail the High Seas until such time as the Distemper abated, no ship speaking them, and no harbour offering them Sanctuary.

September 7.

Tonight I am ashore again, in surroundings so Strange and Horrid that my Heart shrinks within me. This morning we set sail in the path of that mysterious barque, and by noon found ourselves off an Inhabited Island of fairish size, carrying a small village of Dons and a mud Fort with one or two rusty old cannon. As we sailed by it we were intrigued by seeing columns of smoke rising everywhere from the Jungle and hearing a low but very strong and persistent mutter of drums; so that on rounding cautiously a small Cape and coming in sight of the village and fort aforesaid the Captain in command of the Frigate, who is now Admiral of the Fleet in the absence of the Ramillies, flagged all ships and hove to, the Fort lowering its ensign to half-mast and firing a gun. We lay without the harbour bar until a barge puts off, and this comes to us very slowly, nearing us till we see that the rowers were Negroes and that there was only one white man aboard, a young Spanish soldier with a Haggard Face, who as his boat nears us cries out in a dismal cracked voice "That the Yellow Fever was broke out in the town and killing them all; that their Surgeon was Dead of it, and would we in the Name of All Pity send them another Physician?" at which there was much excitement amongst the sailors, they being certain at this news that that ship sighted last night was the Flying Dutchman; only later we learn from the Don that it was not so, but an old coaster that had come to them from another island that morning at dawn, but on hearing the News of the Plague, sheered off and made all sail to the North'ards. The Captain of the Frigate speaks kindly to the Don, but dare not ask him aboard, and there is much discussion as to what shall be done; it being only right that we send them off a Surgeon, but it difficult to decide which vessel to send one from. And so the Captain comes aboard us knowing Commander Hamilton, and after some talk I am sent for, and am bid go ashore and aid the Dons; the Captains assuring me that on reaching their destination they would send proper help and all Necessities. My heart did I must confess quail within me at the Prospect Offered, but thought it of no Avail and only Cowardice to Demur; so to my cabbinn, and to pack my few clothes, requesting the Captain to keep those curios bought for my Relatives and send them to England as soon as might be; then to take farewell of Mr. Nadauld, he giving me sundry advice concerning this Tropic Distemper; and so to the decks and into the Spaniard's boat; the seamen, aye, and the Marines all crowding the rail to wish me God-Speed, and shoving forward to shake my hand and clap my shoulders, and Ned Tollit throws after me a stuffed Monkey or Small Ape to keep me in Health; and so we pulled to the shore amongst the Cheers not only of my well-loved sailors but those of every ship in the Squadron.

Lord, my heart was as lead within me, but on reaching the Quay Side I was soon Distracted from my Self-Preoccupation. The streets of the village were empty and steeped in a quiet that bespoke itself as the Final Hush of Death; there were no cheery fowls scratching in the dust, nor curs scratching for fleas; all had been killed, the Don informed me, as being suspected Carriers of the Plague. Then as we plunged more deeply into the lanes the distant thrumming of drums became clearer and my nose was assailed by a Most Hideous Musky Smell; and so we came out to a clearing before the Fort, where there was a Large Hut at the seaward side about which were moving soldiers in their shirt-sleeves, Nuns, and some Negro slaves; and the breeze blew to me a most vile stench from the Hut aforesaid, and there came from it groans and cries most heart-rending and the Don to inform me that this was their present Hospital, it being thought Imprudent to have the same within the walls of the Fort; the gate of which he points out to me at the head of the clearing, and an older man the Commando of the fort coming from it very feeble leaning on a stick; attended by one-two of his Officers; they coming up to me and thanking me with tears for coming to their Help; the Distemper having raged for three weeks now, and decimated half the village and a third of the garrison, and law and order gone by the board, the slaves growing frantic with Terror and so murdering their masters and escaping to the Jungle; where they had resorted to the most barbaric of practises, the greater part of them being Negroes, and offering sacrifice to their Gods and beating drums and crying aloud all day and through the nights to scare away the demons that they were convinced were haunting 'em. And so with the Officer who first brought me ashore to the Hut, and there to meet a Priest who has some knowledge of Physic his name El Silvanya, and he to fall to his knees and give Thanks for my coming. Faith, I could scarce get inside the hut, it was so crowded and so filthy, with the discharges of the patients and the odour of those dying a most foul charnel House.

I did see straightway that one could never hope

to heal the sick in so crowded a place; each depressed his neighbours; and to inform the Don, who bowed gracefully, but did not seem to understand what I was getting at. So with the aid of sundry Negroes and soldiers to carry out those that were dead and those about to die, and to attend the others, many far gone and others distracted in their Wits, crying out and struggling in a Delirium. Thus I have worked all this day, holding a cresset of burning Sulphur to my nostrils to Neutralise the stenches, only emerging at dinner time for a rest, after which, looking out to sea, I did note that the Ramillies had appeared, and was then hull down on the Horizon, the other ships of the Flotilla standing out after her. So my last link with England is gone, and I am marooned upon this Doleful Island where I can see that I shall be lucky to escape, not even with Health, but my Life. All the afternoon again I have been at the Hospital, realising even more fully that we must have a fresh place for the sick; but unable to get any Sense out of the Spaniards, who are Languid with the Complaint and Despair. Do wonder what will become of my shirts and other Laundry; I have had to change tonight, being Vilely Dirty, and put on fresh Linen; and so to write this in my Journal, my only Confidant, Repositary of all my Hopes and Fears. Do note that despite yesterday being Sunday I did not mention the fact that a small service was held by Commander

Hamilton; shall read in my Testament tonight before retiring for Consolation and a little Penance for this Forgetfulness.

September 8.

Too weary tonight to write much in this my Faithful Diary. Have been to the Captain of the Garrison to urge on him that we must have another Hospital, but he merely shakes his head and says that the slaves will not build one even if we had the materials; and more in the same strain; all the heart has been taken out of him by this Scourge. There are but few drugs either; Lord, Lord, what a pass to be in!

September 9.

Two soldiers of the Garrison died this morning. The Don that brought me ashore to this Accurs'd Island of Grand Palmas heavy-headed; do fear that he has got the Plague. I see that I shall be lucky if I last a week; not only does the Yellow Fever threaten a man, but the climate is hot and damp, enervating one's Vitality; and there are swarms of Miserable Insects, attracted by the Stenches of the Hospital, that plague one everywhere; they have pursued me even into my chamber here within the Officer's Quarters against the Wall of the Fort; one cannot obtain Rest for the Constant thudding of those Cursed Drums.

September 10.

The sick die daily, and even the healthy, as they go about their business, fall to rise no more. Despite all my efforts the Scourge still rages; my heart despairs, naught that I can do seems to prevail against the March of the Distemper; it would seem almost that Fate had in mind to wipe the Island clean of all Human Beings. We have but few drugs, and these mostly harmless Simples; but then this Plague would not seem to be a simple Fever, but more a Hepatic Complaint, the Liver rotting in a manner analogous to the rotting of the skin found in Lepers; the Peruvian Bark therefore seems to have little effect, as Mr. Nadauld did warn me, and as I have since found. There is a period of Malaise and Languor which lasts on an average some five or six days; then Fever appears with pains in the Front of the Head and the Back and Loins; the sufferer's belly is Tender, and he commences to Vomit; his face turns yellow with the Jaundice, and his miserable state rises to a Fury where his Pulse races and his urine grows scanty and his Sweats increase; this is the crisis, and is marked especially by the Tongue, which becomes covered with a thick white scum that leaves the Tip uncovered and a bright red in colour. From this condition the patient may bestir himself, the belly pain diminishing and the Temperature slowly dropping; the yellow tint of his face and eyes and chest decreases and within two or three weeks he is well again and able to move about his duties, though woefully weak and thin. But in others the Vomit turns bloody, even to a colour like Coffee grounds, which may be preceded by a White Ropy Vomit; blood is discharged also from the nose and in the stools; and from the Vehemence of his Emesis the White Scum is reft from his tongue and it becomes Raw and crusted with bloody scabs. Delirium sets in most frequently at this stage, or if the Body's Antics be violent the sufferer sinks suddenly into a Collapse and so into a Coma in which it is hard to tell when he be dead. Not all die in this manner; the disease is running an Acute course, hastened no doubt by the Humidness of the Atmosphere, and many die sudden within a few hours of the onset of Symptoms; others from the Hæmorrhage or from the Pain of their Body's Motions, their Heart failing them in a Syncope even as they Vomit.

All that I can do to aid 'em is to keep the bowels clear at the onset of the complaint, the Peruvian Bark as I have said having no effect, at least any that I can mark, then as the Fever rises to make use of Diaphoretics, to wit Turpentine, Alcohol, Salts of Antimony and Oil of Cinnamon or Cloves mixed together or as many as may be got; to check the Vomiting with Poppy-Flower Water and the Alkaline Earth and to relieve the Pains in the Epigastrium, and thereby to Ease the Congestion in the Liver, with Mercury and Cantharidine Blisters.

The ancients do recommend that in these Hepatic Disorders use be made of Dried and Powdered Earthworms, two drams, Goose dung one dram, in half-an-ounce of Saffras Water, to be taken at a draught; but I have no means of obtaining any of these, and also the disease rages too Ferociously for such gentle treatment to be of avail. The one drug, if it may so be called, that does appear to be of use in this Yellow Fever is Alcohol; it makes 'em sweat, and it Rallies the Flagging Energies; so that most of my patients have been dosed liberally with rum, I at the same time seeing that their bowels are gently eased with half-ounces of the Epsom Salts or ten grains of Jalap; bleeding them of course as need arises. The worthy Priest has been most Helpful, and being a priest has served two purposes; to ease the bodies of the living, and the minds of the dying; between the two he is kept busy; town citizens, soldiers, slaves, all are dying not by twos and threes, but in half-dozens and dozens.

September 11.

The Spanish Officer that brought me ashore, Don Ernesto by name, very sick this morning; his pulse yesterday rapid today slow and weak from his having vomited all night and thereby exhausted his Energy. He is bleeding from the gums and nose; do fear me that his days are numbered. Gave him of my best attention, and so to the others; three more wights died during the night, a soldier and two Negroes. After dinner in Despair to the Fort Commander to insist that he build me some new shelter for my sick, the present one now growing Impossible to work in, the walls coated with dried blood and other discharges, and the flies swarming therein, vile waspish creatures called Tiger Musketeers and bloated Blue-flies, and Midges and such Innumerable. I informed him that I would attend no more sick until I had a new Hospital; so after some discussion he and his other officers to summon the soldiers, and they to turn the Negro Slaves to chopping down palm-trees to make a new hut; and one Negro to refuse, saying that "It was of no avail! They were all dead men!" and so, he proving obdurate, the Captain did draw a pistol from his sash, and shot him through the body; then his men setting on the other slaves with their whips, they were constrained to get to work. So tonight as I took the air on the Clearing I have the satisfaction of seeing a new house already half-built, nearly ready for my sick.

September 12.

The new Hospital completed today, and to get the sick into it, and they being all safely moved, I without any man's consent did set fire to the Old Hut, so that it was consumed to ashes; and some talk thereat amongst the Spaniards, who I know well would have left it either to stand, thereby breeding fresh Pestilence, or used it for a Stores Cabbinn; they being a most slovenly and improvident crew, even the Captain despite his fine manners and long line of Ancestors. Don Ernesto still alive; his vomiting has ceased; if he can rally he may recover, though the dice are loaded against him.

September 13.

Sunday, and the Priest into the town to ring the bell of the Parish Church, aided in this by the surviving Sisters of the small Convent adjoining the Cathedral. Did repair thither with two of the Officers of the Garrison, meeting a few citizens, but not many, for in such a time as this each keeps to himself; neighbour is suspicious of neighbour, and brothers fear lest their own kin may carry the Distemper. Our walk was diverted by the sound of most Doleful Howls and Wails coming from within a fine house set in its own grounds; at which I called a halt, and was about to enter thither, when one Soldier says that the house is that of one Yusuf, an Arab slave Dealer, a Heathen, and therefore one who if as we suspected had the Plague was best left to die; but I did think this most Unchristian Counsel, and set my hand on the gate; at which the Officer who had spoken says that like all Englishmen I was mad, and so shrugs his shoulders and leaves us; the other Officer also shrugging his shoulders, but twirling his moustache and saying that Death would come for each man at a Set Time, and that if this was the day appointed for him to die he was ready to face his Maker like a true knight; and so accompanies me through the gardens to the door of the house. This we found open, and entering found no one within, but passing to the back did there find an elderly woman clad in Eastern dress on her knees on the floor, weeping and tearing her hair; but being unable to get sense from her, and the Howls now being louder, we did pass once more from the house into a Yard at the back, to the Slaves quarters and the stables.

And within one of these we did find the Lord of the house all demented in a Fury beating a patient cow, crying out in his own tongue and in Spanish "Oh cow! Oh beautiful cow! Take away from me upon thyself the sickness that now torments me!"— these heathen having, I learn, a Conviction that disease may be passed by various ways from a master to the various beasts that he owns. The Moor was wielding a thick cudgel and belabouring the poor beast most unmercifully, so that its head already ran with blood. Seeing the man so demented I did seize him and endeavour to wrest the stick from his grasp; on which he grappled me, calling me Azrael and the Angel of Darkness and other names, so that I was hard put to it not to be thrown down. The Spanish officer however, whose courage had risen in proportion as he found he had only a Crazed Man to deal with, coolly unsheathes his sword and stuns the Moor with its hilt; so that he tumbled into a corner, and I knelt to attend him. I did find him feverish, so to take out my Lancet and bleed him; and then carried him into the house and directed by the woman to an upper room, where we laid him on a couch. Then seeing that there was little that I could do further for him, and not thinking that he had the Yellow Fever—though faith it was hard to detect, for the yellow of jaundice would scarce show through his dusky skin—and the woman kneeling by him and ministering to him, I did return to the Stable to take a peek at the cow; and found it very badly hurt; so I did once more return indoors, and finding the Officer gazing at a fountain in a court, did borrow from him the pistol in his belt, and so returning put the cow out of its wretched state.

The woman came down, and with the aid of the Officer I spoke to her and desired her to keep watch over her Lord, and should he become worse, to repair to me at the Fort with all speed; informing her however that I did not consider he had catched the Plague, but was taken with a sudden Apoplexy from the Heat and the Tenseness of the Atmosphere all quivering with the drum beats of those Vile Negroes and Heavy with the Miasma of Death. And so to wash my hands in the fountain and return his pistol to the Don, and then with him once more to set our feet towards the Church; entering it under cover of a Hymn, and so to our seats. The Priest did preach a Tolerable Fine Sermon, calling on all to repent before the Distemper called them to Render Final Account; did at first think he had a mighty fine number of people to preach to, but a further view did show me that the crowding of the Church was due not to the number of people in it, but the distance they sat from each other, all being Terrified of Catching the Distemper from those that sat about them. The service did pass without Incident, though the Spanish Officer informs me that last Sunday a man and a woman dropped from their seats and so being carried out were found to have the Yellow Fever, and so were taken to their homes, where they died a day or two later.

The service finishing I walked back to my quarters with the Officer and the Priest, and to acquaint the latter of what had befallen me as I walked to Church that morning; and he to inform me that such Superstitions were common in the Island, especially amongst the poorer folk and the Negro and Native Slaves; the Negroes especially having many strange Phantasies, to wit, when Pestilence breaks out in their homes they catch a monkey and dress it in fine cloathes; then lead it on a string to each house, so that it may catch the Devils they suppose to lurk within, they beating the walls and floors of the houses to drive out any such; then when the monkey has made the round, he is led to the outskirts of the village, where he is disembowelled and crucified that the aforesaid Devils, having been coaxed out from the hamlet, may feed upon his entrails and so be distracted from returning to the houses.

Others again, when they find themselves particularly affected, beat their animals that the sickness may be diverted from their bodies to the animal; others again catch a toad, spit in its mouth, and then throw said frog away, crying aloud "Oh Frog! Carry my sickness from me!" When the Yellow Fever first broke out, the Negroes did beat old tins, and fire off what guns they could find, and howled aloud, hoping in this manner to frighten the Demon of Illness from their homes; and the young men ran out into the Jungle, crying and wailing, that the Demons aforesaid might follow them; and so returned home again, where they slew all the fowls of the village, that their crowing might not reveal to the Demons where their homes were; that the Demons might be lost, and so the hamlets rid of the Pestilence. This then was the reason why there was no cheerful cuckling of cockerels about the township; the Negroes had killed them all, and the Spaniards the dogs and cats, suspecting these last of being Pest Carriers; so that it was a very empty and soundless village. I did enquire of the Priest why therefore all the animals were not slain, as surely it was as sensible to suspect a cow of carrying the distemper as the smaller dog; to this he replied that the Contagion was supposed to cling about their long fur; but to this I replied that surely the coat of asses and horses and kine, if not as long, was as thick? To which he made no reply, the fact being I suppose that dogs getting the Hydrophoby and cats being suspected of acting on occasion as Witch's help-mates, these Smaller Carnivores are allowed to exist only on Sufferance, and are the first to suffer when Man, frighted by An Epidemic, seeks a Scapegoat.

This afternoon it has come on to rain most dismally, and I not pleased thereat, as the dampness is like to seize my patients already lowered with Fever with Pneumonia and the Screws and the like Distempers of Dampness.

Don Ernesto will live, I think, being of a most stubborn and dogged Constitution; always supposing that he does not catch fresh Disease from the damp. Tonight has come without word from the woman of the Moor. So I suppose he is now cooled of his Madness and once more Sane.

September 15.

Have not wrote in this my Journal these latter days, there being naught to record but woe and misery. The sickness still rages furiously; on Monday the 13th. one of the Nuns assisting me in the Hospital cabin was taken sudden with violent pains across her midriff and I to do all that Art desires to guard the Yellow Fever from her; but by the afternoon she had begun to Vomit; her temperature rose to an extreme height, so that by dusk she was muttering in a Delirium, and by midnight already far down the Long Dark Lane of Death; and so she died the following morning, and her Sisters to perform the Last Rites and put candles about her bed; though for these they had little time, for the rain as I dreaded has caused the Sickness to increase, and three Negroes and a trooper of the garrison kept the Nun company on her Voyage through Space to the Throne; may they all find mercy. I am distracted in my mind about the townsfolk; the Sickness rages in their homes even as it does up here by the Fort; but few can be persuaded to come here for treatment; preferring to perish miserably if they can die with their families about them. This does of course increase my Work, for all these differing houses are but Posting Houses for the Plague, from whence the Distemper spreads to others, as tainted meat infects that adjacent to it; so that I have no real knowledge of how the Disease goes, whether it is abating or increasing. I would to the Officers and to ask that they should impose a quarantine upon the houses composing this little township, and Searchers thereto, that the health of all might be Watched, and in those houses where the Yellow Fever has broken out the sufferers be carried to me and the house closed and fumigated with Burning Sulphur. But these Dons in authority are as childish as the Negroes they affect to despise for their superstitions; saying, like the Negro that the Commandant shot "That they were all Doomed Men; let us eat then and be gay, for Tomorrow we die" and so passing their time drinking and wenching, their Reasoning thereby at the Level of the Beast, for surely it must be obvious to a man of but mean Intelligence that such Debauches will exhaust their Vitality, and so render them easier prey to the Fever should it fasten upon them.

September 16.

My birthday. God, what irony is summed up in those two words! My birthday! The day on which one rejoices, thanking God for the gift of Life, and one's parents or relatives for their due care of one since birth. Yet, on reflection, do see that this mood is but Cowardice and Basest Ingratitude; for each is here to work out his Own Salvation and all the Daily Experiences are but means of testing one's worth; so that I should rejoice, that God cares enough for me to give me this Fine Chance of Showing my Worthiness; this being marooned here and left alone to Battle, aye, with Death, for the bodies of wights more helpless, perhaps more unfortunate, than myself, but one of those trials to which all in greater or lesser degree are subjected from their earliest days to their death bed. Certain it is that there is in Disease, especially in such an Epidemic Plague as this Yellow Fever, a quantity of Grim Malignancy finely calculated to strike Terror to the heart of poor puny Man; yet, when we realise that all these things are in the Hands of God and that one can only do one's duty to the best that is in one, and so doing cast all care upon His Mighty Shoulders, this Vicious Malignancy is seen to be naught but a lantern-lit turnip head; a Mask, shielding, if we could only have faith, one of the Best of Friends. And so no more of this Dolour; let me to my knees this birthday to thank God for all His Loving Kindness to me through all my days, and for this chance to show how much I appreciate all these His gifts to me; and to ask Him that the Scourge may soon be lifted from this Most Unhappy Island, for it still rages with the Utmost Fury.

September 18.

Shall I be thought weak and no true Physician if I confess that the greater part of last night I spent upon my knees in prayer? This I know, that I fell asleep at last more Calm than I have been for many days past, and awoke this morning Vastly Strengthened, so that after breakfast I strode into the Commandant's quarters, and had speech with him; saying that on such an occasion as this I was the Real

Captain and Governor of the Island, and that I insisted that the houses of the town be quarantined, and watchers appointed to spy diligently for new cases of the sickness in the homes of the citizens; at which he plucked at his beard, eyeing me askance; and so bid me come with him to the Dining Hall, where we found the greater part of his Officers gathered drinking and gaming, and he to acquaint them of what I desired; at which there was much talk, and some threatening looks at me. But the worthy Don Ernesto, who had caused his bed to be carried into the Hall that he might throw the dice and otherwise amuse himself to pass the days, speaks up from his pallet, crying "Shame upon them!" and adding that I "was the only Man amongst them; were they, as true subjects of His Catholic Majesty the King of Spain, to allow a mere British Naval Surgeon to teach them their duty?" at which there was more talk, and then the Dons, plucking up some sort of Desp'rate Courage, all begin to shout "No! No!" and so out on to the Parade Ground; where having kicked the Drummer awake, he being in a Drunken Sleep, they gathered what soldiers are left alive, and so down into the town, where they caused a Proclamation to be read that in this time of Universal Distemper each man's house was to be open day and night for Inspection by Duly Appointed Searchers; the which caused some talk, but the Citizens, being Depressed by the Presence of the Contagion, and over-awed by the soldiers, did I think welcome even this Temporary Loss of Independance and Personal Liberty; and so I to stand up by the town-cryer and to acquaint all for the reason of this new Regulation; so that there was no more talk, and all did agree, and we set to work to choose worthy and Honest men to act as Searchers.

Thus tonight I have the satisfaction of seeing the town properly Policed and though it will not, I can see, be possible to get all sick to agree to come for Treatment to the Hospital, yet I have now a means of knowing those places in the town where sickness exists and so can hurry to them and by treatment and the cleansing of the house by Fumigation endeavour to check it's spread to neighbouring homes. So I am given another weapon, though of necessity a somewhat Blunt One, with which to battle this Vile and Loathly Contagion.

September 20.

Sunday, and to church, where I was greeted respectfully by those citizens present, and one Negro woman to attempt to kiss my foot. There is, may God be thanked, a new Atmosphere abroad; folk have plucked up that Courage which is better guard against any Distemper than the Finest Bottles of Physic.

September 21.

This day was called in haste to attend the Horse-Leech of the Garrison, and found him to my Horror afflicted not with the Yellow Fever, but with that Equine complaint so contagious to Humans, the Pulmonary Disease the Farcy or Glanders. The fool acquaints me that it broke out amongst the Troopers Horses nigh a week back; and that he has been endeavouring to stem its course: with the result that I now see, he being very ill and will probably die, this Disease of Glanders being Virulent enough to Horses, but Deadly to Man. But there, I should not rail at him; he was but trying to do his duty, and is a pleasant and worthy man enough; being a Frenchman of good family trained in the School of Animal Medicine at (I think) Montpelier; exiled from his country for his Political Views; and so driven far abroad to earn a living amongst strangers by the exercise of his Art. I did have interesting converse with him, finding that his studies in Animal Anatomy, Physiology and Physic followed a course very similar to that obtaining in my school, or that of any Hospital; having indeed worked in an Infirmary together with those studying Human Anatomy, but he prosecuting researches on the Animal Economy under a Professor interested. Did all that I could to relieve his complaint; did at first search his body for a wound by which the Contagion might have entered, but desisted on his informing me that a horse dying with the disease had sneezed in his eye four days since; and so the disease now coming to a head in him, the Buds forming beneath his skin and one or two commencing to ulcerate; the sites of these eruptions I did blister, and laved the eye infected with Mandregora Water: and he having of course Fever, and the pains in the joints and limbs often found in these Acute Disorders, I did bleed him fifteen ounces, and opened his bowels with ten grains of Gamboge and the same dose of Jalap powdered in Buckthorn Julep; administered also a bolus containing the Peruvian Bark powdered —though this I fear me will be of small effect—and for the Nasal Discharges a Tincture of Honey and Balsamic Syrup that the crusts of the discharge might be eased; and for the better relief of his Bronchia some Paregoric Draught, to wit Black Cherry Water, Extract of the White Poppy of each one dram infused in a sufficient quantity of Sugar and Water; not having by me that Compound Peony Water with which the Ancients did desire this mixture to be compounded; blistered his chest, and so left him, trusting that all would go well.

The searchers have proved diligent; they did mistake this Farcy case for one of the Yellow Fever, misled by the pains in the horse-leech's limbs, but finding besides three cases of the Actual Complaint in sundry of the citizens' homes; to which I hurried in turn, doing all that I could, and in the second house finishing the last grains of Jalap; so that not being over-fond of Gamboge must hence-forth rely on Senna; which is annoying, for the Watery Infusion of these pods doth oft make the patient vomit, a thing to be avoided in this Hepatic Revolt.

September 22.

Trouble today in the town. A searcher, going through the Native's quarters with a Helper, did hear groans coming from a hut, and thereupon did enter, finding to his great horror that there were a dozen or more blacks gathered within, and they cutting the throat of an old man who had the Yellow Fever, that he might die the quicker and the Devil they were convinced was haunting him be diverted by the sight of blood and so be appeased and leave them all. The blacks were greatly wroth at this intrusion of white folk upon their secret ceremonies, and did set upon the Searcher and his companion, and beat them about the head and body so that the Searcher was killed and the companion escaped only with terrible Injuries from which he died tonight; rushing up here, crying most dismal, to the Fort and so into the Officers quarters, demanding instant justice upon the Negroes; upon which they did seek out their Commander and after that delay and wordy talk in which it seems these Dons must ever participate before anything is done, did gather the soldiers and go down into the town to the Negro quarter; where they shot three blacks, and then the Slaves rising upon them were beaten back to the fort; so that I am like to get little sleep tonight for the noise these blacks are making, they breaking into the houses and shops and drinking and looting, and the citizens firing off pistols and muskets at 'em. The soldiers have been aroused from their lethargy by this Defeat, and are manfully striving to hold these slaves in check; but of the eighty soldiers originally here eighteen are dead with the Plague and there are another score in the Hospital here under my charge; and of those that are performing their duty sundry are weak either with recovery from the Fever or with its approach; the blacks on the other hand not being so gravely affected by the Disease, having it would seem a certain degree of Immunity; being exposed to its baleful influence from their early years, and so acquiring a form of Bodily Disdain analagous to that seen in those Inoculated against the Small Pox. There must be I should imagine a round hundred of them, and though they be poorly armed, yet being desperate with Terror they are likely to give us much work to keep 'em within Lawful Bounds.

I have this night therefore been called several times from my attendance at the Hospital Cabbinn to treat various Injuries from swords and pistol bullets and the like; I have seen no one as yet (save the poor Searcher's Companion) hurt grievous; he had a slash over the head that had cut the skull open to the brain. The succouring of these wounded did remind me of the days that I was ship's Chirurgeon, and in particular of that most bloody sea-fight; and to wonder thereby where my shipmates are now, and what they be doing. No ship has come of late into the Harbour; I fear me that that scurvy coaster has spread word of our Distress over all the Seas, so that none will approach until they see the Standard flying full mast-head high from the flag-staff; three ships, coasters, and one French merchantman have been seen since I came here, and a gun fired at 'em for help; but they made no reply, but set all sails and so vanished from sight over the horizon. So we are marooned as truly as though we were shipwrecked on some wild lonely coast; with indeed less hope.

September 23.

The riot was checked last night, but the trouble has by no means been settled. The Negroes retired, bearing with them a white woman, a supposed virgin, and have carried her off into the Jungle there to make sacrifice of her to their Hellish Ju-Ju, this being the name they have given to their God; the Priest distressed thereby beyond all telling, all his labours in teaching them of the One Eternal Merciful God going for naught. The Commandant has set off mighty fierce with what remains of his soldiers and the greater part of the citizens to bring the wench back; the Priest has gone with them, so that today I have laboured with my sick alone, save for the help of the five Nuns left alive.

September 24.

Today summoned into the town to deliver a woman, which I did after three hours hard toil and much sweating.

September 25.

The Farcy case does tolerably well. If he grows no better he grows no worse.

September 27.

Rose this morning with some internal misgivings; the Commandant had not then returned with his men, and did wonder whether the Jungle had swallowed them up. Being Sunday, the Nuns did ring the church bells, but the priest being away and his curate dead three weeks back of the Fever there was no service. I did repair to the church and rested in its cool some little while; praying and reflecting on all that had befallen me; and roused therefrom by a sharp bite from one of those Dam'd Tiger Muske-teers, and so after a few minutes to take my hat and back to the Fort. The Commandant did return after dinner, and he and his company in a Most Doleful State; seven soldiers killed and four citizens, by the Fury of the Negroes; so that the women of the town, who had run out to welcome them, soon fell from huzza-ing to weeping and lamenting. Nine other soldiers were wounded, and eleven citizens; these last not being trained in war had been roughly handled. I have had my hands full with these injured until now; the most part suffering from sword and hatchet cuts about the head and shoulders and arms; which I closed with plaster, bleeding each one for the good of his health; one soldier has had the knee joint exposed, so that in this Humid Miasmatic Climate he will surely die; two of the citizens are badly hurt, one with his ear severed the cut having swept down to bite into the muscles of the neck; the other has lost the first two fingers of his right hand; these were crushed by a cudgel blow the man's hand then gripping a sword, so that for fear of the whole man's hand mortifying he did chop them off without further ado; but their stumps are most foul, so that despite poulticing and blistering I am afraid the Gangrene will set in, and so he will die. I learn that it is almost always fatal to Amputate a Limb or Digit in these Isles; they always mortify most furiously, and the patient's condition being already lowered by the Enervating Air, he soon sinks to rally no more. My hands therefore are tied; even if the wound reaches that condition that would evoke desire to Amputate in other happier conditions I do not think that I will inflict further pain and worry on the fellow, but let him sink quiet to his grave.

The Expedition has however been successful in that it has achieved its object and brought back the wench; so that all are pleased, even the wounded considering their wounds small cost to rescuing a White Lady from the Hideous Perils of being catched by Blacks.

No more of this tonight; my hand pains me; the bite of that Vile Musquito itches and burns intolerably; I think it must have had venom in Its Sting: shall poultice the site ere I seek my couch.

September 28.

The sickness I believe is abating somewhat; if this be true let all thanks be given to God. Have had a wearisome headache all today; shall to bed.

September 29.

God is merciful. The Lancaster was sighted off the island tonight; she now lies without the harbour bar.

September 30.

Tonight I am still ashore, but under what different circumstances! This morning a boat from the Lancaster came ashore, and what was my joy to see in it my very dear friends Mr. Nadauld, Mr. Rose, in charge, and the worthy Ned Tollit, and to hear once more their friendly voices hailing me!

They came ashore and greeted me, the humble

Surgeon's Mate, as though I was the dearest of friends; and so, being greatly shocked at the state of affairs ashore, Mr. Rose went back to the ship to fetch some jolly English sailors and marines to help the Dons keep order; and Mr. Nadauld to assist me, and to approve of all that I had done; and so to work with him in all friendliness, and for my part, all Happiness, through the day. He is on shore for the night, Commander Hamilton having given him leave, and so tonight I can rest in peace, for I have a true comrade to assist me. I must admit that I am more glad of the arrival of my shipmates than I can well describe in cold ink. These last two days I have not been feeling at all myself; have had a headache, and queer shiverings; God in His Mercy grant that I have not catched the Farcy from the horse-leech.

October 2.

Collapsed yesterday when at the Hospital Cabbinn with Mr. Nadauld, being took with a sudden terrible pain across my waist and then a Wild Sweat, and so swooning; came to my senses to find my Superior bending over me with a very Speculative Look in his eye, and to tell him of that dam'd bite I took from the Musketeer; and so he to bleed me, and get me aboard the Lancaster, saying that I had had enough of this Hell Spot, with which I could not well disagree.

So today I lie in my bunk aboard the Lancaster

once more; The Ramillies came into harbour last night with two Spanish Doctors aboard, and all necessities; so that this Island of Grand Palmas is now once more cared for, and my work is done; and I may fold my hands and say "Nunc Dimittis."

October 26.

Much water has flowed beneath Time's bridge since I last made entry in this my Journal. I have been near to Death, and the mark of his bony clutch is still fresh upon me. I escaped only through the skill of my superior Mr. Nadauld and the kindly nursing of my shipmates; may God bless them for all their loving-kindness to me.

When I wrote on Oct. 2 "Nunc Dimittis" I wrote more truly than I realised. My work was done; and my spirit, released from that grim burden of—I may confess it now—Terror that haunted it on the fever stricken Island of Grand Palmas; on which I think I shall never again summon courage to set foot; my spirit, then, strove to wing outwards to Space; I fell into a swoon, so that a sailor entering thought me already dead. He summoned Mr. Nadauld, who coming revived my body, though my mind was still wandering in those Eerie regions of Outer Space. I recognised none of those ministering to me; and I can only glean idea of what then happened to me from what I learn from Mr. Nadauld and my shipmates.

I revived, but only to pass straightway into a Horrid Delirium in which it seemed that I was back on that plague-haunted island, pursued by Spectres of Disaster and Woe, so that I screamed, and shouted aloud "That skulls were all about me! and that Death sat behind them on a throne all draped with a black velvet Pall, waiting to set His Icy Crown about my brows!" and struggled to escape from Him, so that they had to bind me to my bunk lest I do myself an Injury.

From those Loathly Halls, the Ante-Room to the Mansion of Dementia, I escaped at last to lie sane, but weak and languid, as one who has made his peace with God, and only awaits the Final Call. I knew my friends, and had some feeble idea of how much they had striven for me, but I was too weak even to press their hand; only when they spoke anxiously to me trying to cheer me and rouse me the tears ran from my eyes. Not even the news that the Lancaster had been ordered back to England and that we were already half-way there could rouse me to any permanent interest. Slowly however my strength crept back to me and the blood began to run with its customary force through my arteries, so that today for the first time I am able to sit propped up in my bunk and hold pen in my fist. They will not let me look in a mirror yet; I think I can guess the reason, for it was the Yellow Fever that seized upon me, and it has filched all the flesh from my limbs so that they appear as sticks; my hair too has gone, at least the major part, so that I must look a most woe-begone scare crow and they no doubt fear lest sight of myself may give that final shock that will dissipate the last of my Vitality.

October 27.

Would have wrote more yesterday, only Mr. Nadauld entering did take the pen from my fingers and scold that sailor who had given the Journal to me, saying that I was to be as a babe, and think of nothing, only rest and soak in the fresh sea-breezes, as a tree drowsily gathers strength from the sun. We have long left the Bahamas behind, and approach the Azores.

October 29.

We lie at the Azores. There we found lying a Seventy Gun Battleship and Mr. Nadauld has gone aboard of her, this I learn having been arranged since we left Barbados. An apothecary has taken his place until such time as we reach England. He did bid me farewell, saying that he had spoken concerning that Appointment of Chief Surgeon which he mentioned when first I came on ship, to our Captain Commander Hamilton, and that he would speak to the Admiralty concerning it; and when I strove to thank him for all his kindness to me, smilingly laid a hand on my mouth, and so went on deck; and

I very downcast thereat, for I have suspicion that I may never see him more.

November 4.

There is little to enter in this Journal these latter days. We are out on the bosom of the Atlantic, our next port England; and all the sailors have been very joyful thereat, and there has been much singing. It was indeed delightful to lie here in my bunk last Sunday, and listen to the cheery united voices of the ship's company singing away most lustily at their Hymns, reflecting the while of that last service I attended in the Cathedral at Grand Palmas; wondering the while how things go now in that unhappy spot.

November 7.

Sunday, and to my feet this day and so up on deck assisted most kindly by two Marines, to be greeted kindly by Mr. Rose and the Captain, Mr. Butler, Ned Tollit; all my old and dear friends. I was not allowed to attend service, as it was thought this might tire me unduly; but I followed it as best I might from below decks, and gave most hearty thanks that I was now recovered from my Distemper.

November 12.

We draw near home. Sighted several English merchantmen these days past.

November 14.

Sunday; attended service.

November 16.

Gales and rain, but the sturdy vessel forges doggedly on her path. Today we sighted the Scilly Isles, and wild Huzza-ing from all the sailors, the Watch Below swarming up on deck at the Hail of the Look-Out "Land Ahoy!" and so rushing up the Ratlines and along the bow-sprit like Mad Creatures.

November 17.

Tonight the Lizard lies away on our lee, half-hidden by the mist. We are thus now entering Home Waters.

November 21.

Sunday, and a very solemn service giving Thanks for a speedy and safe voyage; Portland Bill being sighted early this morning.

November 19.

Today we have rounded the Needles and are standing up the sea-channel on the farther side of the Isle of Wight. The wind has been somewhat contrary, to the great Annoyance of Commander Hamilton, who is anxious to get ashore; it seems that some relative has died, and has left him either Money or a Title, or both; he did summon me today to his cabbinn, where after enquiring after my health, he did very kindly give me a letter to some friends of his near Gosport, a Mr. and Mrs. Corder, who kept a large house for the Convalescing of sick officers; he advising me to take a rest there for some months, my health still not being robust, the Fever having left me with a persistent cough; adding also that he would not forget when making report to the Authorities to mention my Service, of which he spoke in the warmest terms, assuring me that thereby I should be promoted Full Surgeon on the Lancaster; for all of which I thanked him deeply.

November 20.

Disaster does ever seem to dog my footsteps. Today we cast anchor off Spithead, and Commander Hamilton being in a great hurry to get ashore to Portsmouth sets off in the cutter with seven men, though the sea was rough, there being much wind. They left the ship with all ease, but mid-way to the shore, the boat being small, they encountered trouble from the waves; and a little further on a sudden clap of wind upset it, turning it completely over; so that my worthy Captain was drowned, together with five of the seven seamen with him. May God rest their souls! Commander Hamilton though brusque was a just man and a worthy; ever sensible that the powers lodged in him were not to be abused and never forgetting that Higher Authority before Whose

Tribunal he is now summoned. His principles were good and his conduct manly. By his death my expectations of being made Full Surgeon are Diminished and Made Remote; but perhaps all that I have done will stand me in good stead when I apply to the Admiralty Board.

November 21.

Sunday, and service taken by Mr. Rose, and he to pray for those drowned.

Some of the officers have gone ashore today; the Lancaster will be here for some time, as her Ordnance requires attention. The Purser has been paying out the monies owing to each; I have received my share, and with what remains of my prize money I have nigh sixty guineas to jingle in my pocket; a fine round sum, giving one a most warming sense of wealth. Have been busy packing my box, not forgetting those little curios I purchased, which I found still present in my cabin when I came to sanity again.

Tomorrow I shall go ashore and take coach for Gosport; no more tonight, am somewhat tired.

ENVOY

JOHN KNYVETON duly went to the "House of Mr. and Mrs. Corder at Gosport" and stayed there for some three weeks. He remarks that "My good constitution, together with wholesome nourishment, and the care of my host and hostess, who were very kind to me, enabled me to make a great stride towards complete recovery"; but, at the end of this time, learning that the Lancaster was ordered to sea, he adds that "I hurried on board still in a weak state, lest I should be left behind, and thrown amongst strangers."

Captain Amherst had succeeded Commander Hamilton in the command of the Lancaster, and, says John Knyveton, "I was recommended to him by the officers": but he was not appointed Full Surgeon, and in the April of the following year was removed on board his old Flagship the Ramillies, she having then returned to St. Helens; this change with a view to promotion, but his pay was thereby lowered to thirty shillings a month.

The Ramillies subsequently cruised in the Mediterranean, where one of the Surgeon's Mates dying of a fever (probably typhoid) John received that promotion that he had been hoping for, and became First Surgeon's Mate.

John Knyveton was a Naval Surgeon until the end of the year 1760, when he was discharged at Plymouth after, as he says, "a wandering, though not disagreeable life, of nine years." During that time he had changed ships six times; being surgeon successively to his first ship the Lancaster (24 guns), the Ramillies (100 guns), the Weazle (a sloop; this appointment lasted only five weeks), the Centaur (20 guns), the Aurora ("a fine frigate of thirty-eight guns commanded by Captain Francis William Drake") and the Edgar—"a new ship of sixty guns," and had sailed to most of the known countries of the world, visiting the Mediterranean and the islands of Minorca and Majorca, and also Gibraltar, with the Ramillies. Finding that he had no chance of further promotion aboard her, he went to London when she returned to England, and through the interest of the Dowager Duchess of Devonshire, to whom he had been of service, being appointed to the Weazle sloop, and after a few weeks aboard her to the Centaur, then sailing to the coast of Guinea, "in company," says John, "with the Lichfield of fifty guns"; touching with her at Teneriffe, and so to the Cape Verde Islands, and "at all the places between Gambia and Ancober." "The journey," says John, "would have been tolerably pleasant, for all were in reasonably good health, though it was the rainy season; and I had money in my pocket which I had no occasion of spending, and my prospects were improving so that it could have been an exceedingly enjoyable voyage, but that the Captain was a very ill-bred man, and continually quarrelling with the officers."

They left the coast of Africa and sailed to Prince's Island, "where we wooded and watered," proceeding then to the West Indies. They cruised in the West Indies for seven months, John passing his time by learning the French language; and were then ordered home with a convoy; on arriving at Portsmouth the Centaur was paid off, and John Knyveton was instantly appointed surgeon to the Aurora. The Aurora did not, however, set sail, but hung about the coast, so that John solicited a testimonial from Captain Drake, and was appointed to the Edgar, with whom he sailed once more to the Mediterranean. War had then broken out with France, and the Edgar cruised off the island of Minorca watching the French squadron, receiving orders after three months to proceed to Villa Franca—which gave John an opportunity of visiting Nice, and "some other parts of Piedmont." The Edgar rejoined the English fleet then cruising off the Spanish coast, and joined action with them in an attack on the French squadron. Two French ships were taken, and the rest scattered. John's Diary here has a very curious entry; he remarks that "The Edgar had been very sickly before this action, but became immediately after it very healthy; which change was attributed to various causes, but I suppose it was owing to her being well fumigated by the firing of the gunpowder": a grim comment on the conditions then existing on board the naval ships, when the common seamen especially were herded for sleep into small low rooms, usually one of the gun-decks, where they slept in hammocks slung about the guns, the feet of one to the head of the other, "so that they received not each other's breath"; when to leave the gunports open was to be soaked with sea-spray, and to close them was to stifle; when as John himself records, "there were not many verminous insects except in the sailors' quarters."

The Aurora returned to England, and subsequently sailed convoy to a fleet of merchantships and transports, in company with the Oxford, Man-of-War, to the West Indies. John went down with a fever again at Havana, returning after many months once more to England where the Edgar was paid off, and John obtained his discharge.

He was by then a man of some substance, being possessed of "upwards of five hundred pounds" and visiting his relatives at Hestley was advised by them to settle ashore in practice. This he did, returning first to London to revise his knowledge by taking a course in Anatomy at St. George's Hospital; then going to Winchester, there being relatives there of Captain Drake, with whom he had been very friendly. But he found too many other doctors there for him to be able to make a reasonable living and so came back once more to London, where he took up his studies again, writing a treatise which on the advice of certain friends he submitted to Aberdeen University, and received the Doctorate of Medicine of Aberdeen University for it. This treatise was on his old and favourite theme, the Puerperal Fever. He subsequently published a pamphlet on the Construction and Use of Vapour Baths; and as he says, "began in one way and another to become fairly well known." He was appointed Surgeon to the William and Mary, one of the King's yachts, but resigned this post after a year, as the vessel was ordered to sea.

He then settled in Oxendon Street, and put up his plate, and did better than he expected; the post of Lecturer in Midwifery to his old school, "Infirmary Hall," being vacant, he applied for it and received it. In 1763 he married Elizabeth Brodie, daughter of an army linen-draper, she bringing with her "no money dowry, but the leasehold of two houses in Vine Street, these producing about eighty pounds a year clear of all deductions."

In the very year that he was married—"thanks to the frugality of my wife"—John saved two hundred pounds, and as a result moved into a larger house in Queen Street, Golden Square. Twin daughters were born a year later, and six years later a son.

John did well in practice, and within two years of his marriage invested in a "chariot with a coachman in a handsome livery and a servant behind"; which, he adds naïvely, "were beyond my wish and inclination; but I thought them due to my present reputation, as well as to my future prospects, and I hoped that I had secured my family from distress, if I were to die before I had an opportunity of making any further addition to my fortune." This last is in reference to a certain purchase of land that he had made in Norfolk.

John Knyveton died at the age of eighty years, on the morning of Saturday the 25th of November, 1809. His son Thomas Knyveton (who was called to the Bar in 1811) records that "he rose at his usual hour and went down to breakfast. To his wife's enquiries after his health he replied that he was 'quite well,' but having occasion to leave the room for a few minutes to get something that she required, she found him on her return stretched upon the floor, and quite insensible. His countenance was tranquil and composed, but all efforts to restore animation were in vain. Not a moment had been allowed for preparation; but what preparation could have better fitted him for the aweful change?"

Let us complete this outline sketch of the subsequent life of the author of what is surely one of the most interesting documents recently brought to light, by taking a further final extract from his son's notes; that in which he gives a thumb-nail portrait of his father:

"In his person," writes Thomas Knyveton, "my father was firm and strongly made, about five feet nine inches tall. His hair, originally chestnut, had turned with age to a silvery white. His complexion was fresh and vigorous, his eye continued remarkably clear and bright, his hearing was unimpaired, and his teeth remained entire to the very last. Such was my father in his eightieth year."

The editor can only add in conclusion, as John himself might have said in similar circumstances, "May he rest in peace"; let us hope that his final summons called him to Faerie Seas where he sails for ever more with Mr. Nadauld, Mr. Rose, Mr. Butler, Ned Tollit, and the rest of his friends in a galleon that never knows storms or the roar of hostile cannon.

GLOSSARY OF SCIENTIFIC NAMES

THE secret of Medicine's tardy awakening from its sleep of centuries is found partly in the loosening of its ecclesiastical bonds, but largely in the development of the microscope. The invention of the latter towards the end of the sixteenth century shed a flood of light into the dark mystery of the ultimate construction of animal and vegetable tissues, and thereby into the associated mysteries of disease, corruption, and death. A microscope stands before the editor as he writes, and as he gazes at it there rise before him out of the mist of the centuries the ghosts of the men who made it possible—ANTONY VAN LEEUWENHOEK (1632-1723), the Dutchman of Delft, the first to see bacteria, justly termed the Father of Microscopy; NEHEMIAH GREW, the Englishman (1641-1712) in his full-bottomed wig, who first differentiated vegetable tissue; HOOKE and REDI and SPALLANZANI, a mighty host passing up through the ages to, nearer our own times, the intellectuals in whose hands it proved the lever that turned the world upside down; PASTEUR, and LISTER, the dearly loved "Chief," who applied his discoveries to the eternal saving of human life; DARWIN, the gentle genius, and his bull-dog HUXLEY.

Van Leeuwenhoek's instrument was a simple hand lens; that of Grew's a cumbersome compound instrument with the lenses set in a tube, similar to those now in the South Kensington Museum. When John Knyveton first inspected Mr. Kelly's two-foot instrument, he little suspected it was the agent that finally would solve all those questions which, as we may read in his Diary, so sorely puzzled him. Those giants he specifically mentions were famous in his day; and it is curious that though they included Dutchmen, Italians, and Frenchmen as well as Britishers, their works were mostly first published in English. They are:

HENRY BAKER, one time President of the Royal Society, author of a work entitled *The Microscope Made Easy,* published in 1742, a copy of which is in the editor's library.

SWAMMERDAM, a Dutchman (1637-1680) whose works were collected after his death and published in 1737-1738 under the title of *The Bible of Nature.* This has rightly been termed the finest collection of microscopical observations ever published by one worker. His plates of the anatomy of the bee and the development of the gnat and dragon-fly are consulted by naturalists to this day.

LYONET, a Dutch lawyer who published in 1740 a famous monograph on the goat-moth, and LESSER, whose remarkable essays on insects are strangely tinged with mysticism.

MARCELLO MALPIGHI (1628-1694), Italian Professor of Medicine at Bologna University, who turned his attention to the bodies in his post-mortem room, and thereby clinched Harvey's description of the circulation of the blood by discovering the invisible capillaries through whch the blood is conveyed through the tissues from artery to vein. His name lives to-day in certain structures which he was the first to describe, such as the knots of blood vessels in the kidney through which the blood is filtered, which are known to every medical student as the Malpighian corpuscles. He also made many important discoveries in the development of the chick, on the anatomy of the silk-worm, and on the anatomy of plants. He possessed a magnificent pathological museum, and stated openly that he regarded his patients largely as future specimens for its shelves.

Hand in hand with these researchers went the men who made their microscopes, the names of whom are largely forgotten. BENJAMIN MARTEN, mentioned in John Knyveton's Diary is one who survives, as are MESSRS. CULPEPER and SCARLETT of many years later. Benjamin Marten and Culpeper and Scarlett, had their shops in Holborn, and all three were noted opticians.

Their example was followed still later, in the eighteen-twenties, by ANDREW PRITCHARD, a watchmaker, one of whose instruments together with his portrait is still preserved in the South Kensington Museum, and whose work on the Infusoria became a classic. The editor is fortunate enough to possess a copy of his work also, together with many older medical works, among them a copy of that Gibson's *Anatomy* favoured by John Knyveton. In their dusty faded pages one may read of the discoveries, fresh then, made by the geniuses mentioned, whose names burn with fire forever from history's golden scroll of honour.

GLOSSARY OF TERMS

Aorta: the great artery of the body, leaving the heart on the left side to run down in front of the backbone to divide in the region of the kidneys into two large vessels supplying the back and lower limbs.

Clyster: enema, given in the eighteenth century with a wooden funnel. (A famous political prisoner imprisoned in the Tower in the sixteenth century was poisoned deliberately by being given when ill a clyster of corrosive sublimate.)

Compound (ed) fracture: where the bone of a limb breaks and projects through the skin.

Costæ: ribs.

Doxy: a slang term for girl of light virtue.

Dug: breast.

Dura mater: a tough membrane, the outer of three enclosing the brain beneath the skull.

Femur: thigh bone.

Fibula: the smaller of two bones composing the leg.

Foxed: drunk, bewildered.

French disease: syphilis. (*See also* Lues venerea.)

High Toby, taking the: becoming a highwayman.

Humerus: the bone of the upper arm.

Ligamentum patellæ: the ligament of the knee-pan, beneath the knee in front of the shin.

Lues venerea: venereal disease, usually syphilis. An

eighteenth-century gentleman was not considered such until he had caught the disease three times. (Also known as the Great Pox.)

Metacarpals: the bones of the hand.

Metatarsals: the bones of the foot.

Optic nerve: the nerve of sight.

Os calcis: the heel bone.

Os pubis: one of three bones forming the pelvic girdle.

Palliasse: a straw mattress.

Paraplegia: paralysis.

Parietal: a flat bone which with its fellow forms part of the side and part of the base of the skull.

Peruvian bark: modern name, Cinchona. From it is extracted quinine.

Phthisica pneumonica: consumption.

Rheum: cold, chill.

Stilet: surgical instrument resembling a sharp-pointed probe.

Stone: accumulations of uric acid and other salts in the bladder and kidneys, either as large masses, or quantities of sand-like material (gravel).

Strabismus: squint.

Tabula vitrea: hard shiny porcelain-like inner surface of the flat bones forming the vault of the skull.

Trocar and cannula: surgical instrument consisting of a sheath and round sharp-pointed rod which slides within the sheath.

Vulva: external generative organs of the female.

(1)